Catalogue produced on occasion of the exhibition:

'ITALIAN PAINTINGS FROM THE 17TH TO THE 18TH CENTURIES'

7 January – 19 February 2011

At SPERONE WESTWATER

257 Bowery, New York 10002

Edited and co-ordinated by: Mira Dimitrova, Angelica Poggi and Marco Voena

Exhibition curated by: Gian Enzo Sperone and Marco Voena

Cover image:

Artemisia Gentileschi, *Portrait of an Unidentified Man*

ITALIAN PAINTINGS

FROM THE 17TH TO THE 18TH CENTURIES

With contributions by:

Francesca Baldassari

Federico Cavalieri

Francesco Frangi

Lisa Goldenberg Stoppato

Bozena Anna Kowalczyk

Judith W. Mann

Denise Maria Pagano

Gianni Papi

Wolfgang Prohaska

ROBILANT+VOENA

CONTENTS

The aim of this exhibition is to present to the public a survey of Italian Old Masters from the 17th and 18th centuries, from Cavalier d'Arpino to Giandomenico Tiepolo. Ninety years after Ugo Ojetti's seminal exhibition, *La Pittura Italiana del Seicento e Settecento* at Palazzo Pitti, Florence, this show intends to reassert the importance within art history of Italian painting in the centuries following the Renaissance. A painting that in its variety and richness concludes the century of Michelangelo, Raphael and Leonardo and in its being "at times theatrical and declaiming, at others virile and immediate, vehement and gracious, vulgar and seductive, tempestuous and serene, here rhythmically composed and balanced in a similar manner to architecture, there frantically disjointed like a cry of passion" (as Ojetti writes) sets forth a foundation for modern painting. It is an art that does not diminish at the end of the 1600s but continues in the Rococò style, "flowers of that robust trunk, of those one hundred branches, here dark, there lit by lamps and flames of the sun", and that leads into the mature painting of the 1700s. It is an art that carries universal values, but is informed by local perspective and personal ideals. It is capable of offering a model for European culture, originally with Caravaggesque painting and a century later with *vedutismo*.

CATALOGUE

GIUSEPPE CESARI CALLED CAVALIER D'ARPINO
Arpino 1568 - 1640 Rome

David with the Head of Goliath, 1598

Oil on canvas
39.4 x 30.1 in / 100 x 76.5 cm
Signed and dated lower right: 1598 IOSEF.A; Inscription on verso: Di mano del Caualier Giuseppe d'Arpino del no 255.

PROVENANCE
Rome, Villa Aldobrandini a Monte Magnanapoli, Cardinal Pietro Aldobrandini (1603);
Rome, Villa Aldobrandini a Monte Magnanapoli, Cardinal Ippolito Aldobrandini (1638);
Rome, Villa Aldobrandini a Monte Magnanapoli, Olimpia Aldobrandini junior (1663, 1682);
Rome, heirs of Vincenzo Camuccini;
Milan, Carlo Orsi (2000);
Koelliker Collection.

EXHIBITIONS
Ariccia, Palazzo Chigi, *Mola e il suo tempo. Pittura di figura a Roma dalla Collezione Koelliker,* 22 January - 23 April 2005, no. 6; Ottawa, National Gallery of Canada, *From Raphael to Carracci. The Art of Papal Rome,* 29 May - 7 September 2009, no. 147.

LITERATURE
F.W.B. Ramdohr, *Über Mahlerei und Bildhauerarbeit für Liebhaber des Schönen in der Kunst,* Leipzig 1787, 3 vols., I, p. 182;
P. della Pergola, "Gli inventari Aldobrandini: l'Inventario del 1682 (II)", in *Arte Antica e Moderna,* 21, vol. VI, 1963, pp. 80, 413;
C. D'Onofrio, "Inventario dei dipinti del cardinal Pietro Aldobrandini compilato da Giovan Battista Agucchi nel 1603", in *Palatino,* 9-12, 1964, pp. 17, 207;
H. Röttgen, In *Cavalier Giuseppe Cesari d'Arpino. Un grande pittore nello splendore della fama e nell'inconsistenza della fortuna,* Rome 2002, pp. 67, 317-318, cat. no. 79;
M.C. Terzaghi, *Un Cavalier d'Arpino al naturale,* in C. Volpi (ed.), *Caravaggio nel IV Centenario della Cappella Contarelli,* Proceedings of International Study Conference (Rome, 24-26 May 2001, ed. by M. Calvesi), Rome 2002, pp. 327-333;
H. Röttgen, in F. Petrucci (ed.), *Mola e il suo tempo. Pittura di figura a Roma dalla Collezione Koelliker,* exhibition catalogue, Milan 2005, pp. 112-113;
S. Schütze, in D. Franklin (ed.), *From Raphael to Carracci. The art of Papal Rome,* exhibition catalogue, Ottawa 2009, pp. 432-433.

By the end of the century, Cardinal Pietro Aldobrandini had become one of Giuseppe Cesari's most important patrons. The artist enjoyed the protection of the cardinal's uncle, Pope Clement VIII (1592-1605) and had a vast clientele. Indeed in 1595 when he was commissioned to fresco the Sala dei Conservatori in the homonymous palazzo in Rome he was described as the *"pictor unicus,*

rarus et excellentis ac primarius".

Our painting was first mentioned in the inventory (1603) of the cardinal's property conserved in the villa at Monte Magnanapoli (D'Onofrio, 1964, p. 207): "A picture with David with the head of the giant Goliath four p. high, in a gilded frame, by Gioseppe d'Arpino, marked no. 255" [the p. stands for the Roman *palmo* that was the equivalent of roughly 22 cm]. The same number appears on the back of the original canvas which came to light when the lining was removed during a recent restoration.

This picture could be one of the paintings for which the artist received a series of payments from the Cardinal between 11 and 24 March 1599 (Terzaghi, 2002).

The picture reappears in the inventory of the property of Ippolito Aldobrandini in 1638 (D'Onofrio, 1964, p. 17) and in the 1663 (D'Onofrio, 1964, p. 207) and 1682 (P. della Pergola, 1963, p. 80) inventories of the junior Olimpia Aldobrandini's assets. It was still in

the Aldobrandini villa in 1787 when Friedrich Wilhelm Basilius von Ramdohr Esso saw it ("David und Goliath, von Cav. d'Arpino"). During the Napoleonic occupation the villa was the residence of the French governor in Rome, General Sextus Alexandre François Miollis. However, in 1814 the painting was no longer in the villa (Cf. *Indicazione delle sculture e della galleria de' quadri esistenti nella villa Miollis al Quirinale,* Rome 1814) and was by then most probably in the hands of Vincenzo Camuccini.

Röttgen writes: "The painting is of very high, harmonious and elegant quality. The youth has a light, soft complexion with golden blonde hair; he is partially dressed in a golden yellow chiton, with a gleaming, transparent azurite blue and white sash, in his right hand he holds his sword, and in the left the hard, stony head of Goliath. The boy's face expresses grief and anger, and clearly recalls Michelangelo's *David*" (Röttgen, 2005, p. 112). The painting - "that dates from the period in which Arpino achieves the maximum softness

Fig 1. Cavalier d'Arpino, *David*, Naples, Certosa di San Martino, sacristy.

in his work, in the colours, the fabrics and the flesh tones" (Röttgen, 2005, p. 112) - is stylistically comparable to the frescoes in the sacristy of the Certosa di San Martino in Naples (1596-1597) - and especially the *David with the Head of Goliath* (Fig. 1), *Judith with the Head of Holofernes and Samson with the Jawbone of an Ass* in the ceiling triangles - and the *Saint Barbara* in the church of Santa Maria in Traspontina, Rome that was unveiled in September 1597. Cesari rarely used the three-quarter view of the torso, and it recalls the position of the *Mocking of Christ* (Fig. 2) in the sacristy of San Carlo ai Catinari in Rome, that is datable in the same year, 1598.

As Maria Cristina Terzaghi (2002) and Sebastian Schütze (2009) noted, we can see hints of Caravaggio's early Roman works in this painting. Merisi worked in Arpino's atelier for nearly one year in 1593 (See G. Mancini, *Considerazioni sulla pittura,* edited by A. Marucchi-L. Salerno, Rome 1956, I, p. 226 and II, pp. 124-125), and there is a definite similarity with Caravaggio's approach in the powerful, naturalistic rendering of David's body, and in the way he seems to look directly at the observer much like the *Sick Bacchus* (Fig. 3) in the Galleria Borghese which had actually belonged to Cesari as we learn from the 1607 inventory drawn up when the Cavalier's property was seized by the authorities.

Fig 2. Cavalier d'Arpino, *Mocking of Christ*, SS. Biagio e Carlo ai Catinari, sacristy.

Fig 3. Caravaggio, *Sick Bacchus*, Rome, Galleria Borghese.

GIUSEPPE CESARI CALLED CAVALIER D'ARPINO

Arpino 1568 - 1640 Rome

Venus and Cupid, 1602 - 1603

Oil on canvas
31.3 x 39.2 in / 79.5 x 99.5 cm

PROVENANCE
Macerata, private collection of a noble family;
Rome, collection of Fabio Failla.

EXHIBITIONS
Rome, Palazzo Venezia, *Il Cavalier D'Arpino,*
June - July 1973, no. 31.

LITERATURE
H. Röttgen, in *Il Cavalier d'Arpino,* exhibition
catalogue, Rome 1973, pp. 109-110;
H. Röttgen, *Il Cavaliere Giuseppe Cesari
d'Arpino. Un grande pittore nello splendore
della fama e nell'incostanza della fortuna,* Rome
2002, p. 113, fig. 61, no. 111, p. 348.
R. Ward Bissell, *Artemisia Gentileschi and the
authority of art,* Pennsylvania State University
Press 1999, pp. 248-249, fig. 134;

Venus is kissing Cupid in an alcove enclosed by a heavy red curtain; the goddess is reclining on a sharply creased white sheet. The background, on the right, is a stormy landscape. This picture is one of group of mythological paintings Cesari did in the very early 1600s. On the basis of the style, Herwarth Röttgen grouped and dated them as more or less contemporaneous with the frescoes of *Scenes from the Old Testament* in Pietro Aldobrandini's Villa Belvedere at Frascati that were painted between July 1602 and February 1603. All of these paintings are characterized by an accentuated roundness of the shapes and sharper lines in the treatment of the folds on the draperies.

Up to that time "Cesari had never devoted himself to mythological paintings with erotic overtones. Moving on from the style of the decorations on the ceiling of the Loggia Orsini, 1594-1595, [where the main figure in the centre panel depicting *Love Vanquishing Pan Crowned by Venus and Juno* (fig. 1) strongly resembles the Cupid in our painting] the artist developed a playful, plump and childlike female type... Now he embraced the public's

Fig 1. Cavalier d'Arpino, *Love vanquishing Pan*, Rome, Palazzo del Pio Sodalizio dei Piceni.

Fig 2. Circle of Daniele da Volterra, *Scipio's Mother with Jupiter in the Guise of a Serpent,* Palazzo dei Conservatori, Throne Room, Rome.

new taste that liked to see mythological [scenes] in an ambiguous atmosphere that combined childlike innocence with eroticism. It is a style that would soon be interpreted by the Bolognese painters as well, such as Domenichino, Albani and even by Annibale Carracci" (Röttgen, 2002, p. 347).

These mythological-erotic paintings can be dated around the period immediately following the artist's trip to Paris in 1600-1601 - as part of Cardinal Pietro Aldobrandini's retinue - and his encounter with the courtly art of the School of Fontainebleau that reinforced his recollections of the slightly affected and formal lessons of late Florentine and Roman Mannerism.

Röttgen (2002, p. 348) identifies the model for our canvas as a scene in a frescoed frieze in the Room of the Tapestries in the Palazzo dei Conservatori in Campidoglio, depicting the *Scipio's Mother with Jupiter in the Guise of a Serpent* (fig. 2). The fresco, dated 1544, seems to be based on the scenes from the history of ancient Rome that Daniele da Volterra had painted in one of the first floor rooms of Palazzo Massimo alle Colonne around 1538-1543 (See S. Guarino-P. Masini (ed.), *Gli affreschi del Palazzo dei Conservatori,* Milan 2008, p. 65). The goddess's pose is a perfect match with our painting, only here we see Cupid in place of the serpent. Cesari was certainly familiar with the frescoes in the Room of the Tapestries - subsequently renamed the Throne Room - because he started work on the decorations in the Conservators' Room of the same palace in 1596.

Furthermore, Röttgen sees similarities between the structure of the goddess's head and the figure of Diana in *Diana and Actaeon* (fig. 3) which is in the Louvre and, in his opinion, was done in 1602/1603, like the painting presented here.

Cesari revisited the subject of this painting a few years later in *Venus Reclining with Two Cupids* (oil on panel, 42 x 61.5 cm) that was in the Mauro Herlizka collection

in New York (Röttgen, 2002, p. 446). The arrangement is analogous to the painting here: Venus is reclining on white sheets and the legs and torso are in similar positions. However, the position of the head is different, in the American painting it is turned towards the right shoulder to look at one of the two Cupids. The landscape beyond the window is also different, framed by a column and a sill "accentuating the reference to Titian's famous Venuses... This piquant painting is executed with lively brushstrokes with several *pentimenti,* on the whole it is a much faster painting than the picture that was in the Failla collection". According to Röttgen, it can be dated in the 1620s.

Finally, from Röttgen we learn that the 1624 inventory drawn up at the death of Monsignor Costanzo Patrizi, pontifical treasurer of the Apostolic Camera, includes two paintings by the Cavalier d'Arpino either of which - particularly the latter - could be the one shown here. Under the heading *"Nell'altra stanza del guercio"* are the descriptions of these two paintings, one after the other: "A picture of a Venus with a satire of Love by the hand of Cavalier Giuseppe with a gilded frame, 100 *scudi"*; "Another of Venus and Cupid by the same hand with a frame decorated with gold, 200 *scudi"* (see also A.M. Pedrocchi, *Le stanze del tesoriere. La quadreria Patrizi: cultura senese nella storia del collezionismo romano del Seicento,* Milan 2000, p. 387).

"Thanks to paintings such as this [*Venus and Cupid* shown here] Cesari's fame spread throughout Europe". There was such demand for his work that "on 10 January 1603, while the Cavaliere was working on the frescoes at Frascati, Cardinal Pietro Aldobrandini informed cardinal Dietrichstein that the desire of the Emperor Rudolf II to have a painting by Cesari could not be fulfilled at that time" (Röttgen, 2002, p. 113).

Fig 3. Cavalier d'Arpino, *Diana and Actaeon,* Paris, Musée du Louvre.

GIOVAN BATTISTA CRESPI CALLED IL CERANO
Cerano ca. 1567-1568 - 1632 Milan

Christ and the Samaritan Woman at the Well, 1615 - 1620

Oil on panel
39.4 x 28.3 in / 100 x 72 cm

INSCRIPTION
Verso - *"Il Conte Santa fede / napoli"*, and fragments of seals.

PROVENANCE
Vienna, possibly Liechtenstein Collection
Manchester, District Bank, after 1945
National Westminster Bank Collection, after 1970
Banbury, Heythrop Park
London, Colnaghi, 1994
Koelliker collection.

EXHIBITIONS
Milan, Palazzo Reale, *Maestri del '600 e del '700 lombardo nella Collezione Koelliker,* 1st April – 2nd July 2006.

LITERATURE
P. Cannon Brookes, *Lombard Painting c. 1595 - c. 1630: The age of Federico Borromeo,* exhibition catalogue, Birmingham 1974, pp. 112-113;
M. Rosci, Crespi Giovan Battista, in *Dizionario Biografico degli italiani,* XXX, Rome 1984, p. 708;
D. Garstang, in *Master Paintings,* exhibition catalogue (Colnaghi, London), London 1994, pp. 38-41, n. 6;
A. Morandotti (ed.), *Pittura italiana antica. Artisti e opere del Seicento e del Settecento,* Milan 1995, p. 129;
M. Rosci, *Il Cerano,* Milan 1999, pp. 214-217, n. 137;
F. Cavalieri, in A. Morandotti-F. Frangi (ed.), *Dipinti lombardi del Seicento. Collezione Koelliker,* Turin 2004, pp. 30-33;
F. Cavalieri, in A. Morandotti-F. Frangi (ed.), *Maestri del '600 e del '700 lombardo nella Collezione Koelliker,* exhibition catalogue, Milan 2006, pp. 34-37.

In front of a rocky wall, with scattered plants, that is the backdrop to the well, the seated Christ turns to the Samaritan woman who has put one copper bucket on the ground and is holding another in her right hand. On the left there is a narrow, but very deep view of distant mountains, houses and a castle; two men engaged in conversation are approaching.

The good state of conservation makes it possible to appreciate the way the artist exploits the wooden support that shows through, giving the paint surface a particular, almost enamel-like sheen. There is no definite information about where the painting was originally located. Sir Thomas Barlow purchased it for the District

Bank's Manchester office after World War II when he was president of that institution; then, after the merger with the National Westminster Bank it became part of the assets of the latter. According to the contents of a handwritten note by Sir Barlow, the painting was originally in the Liechenstein Collection and came from Vienna (Cannon-Brookes, 1974). The inscription on the back ("Il Conte Santa fede / napoli"), where there are also some fragments of seals, would attest to a passage through Naples at some undetermined time.

There are other, nearly identical, versions of this composition in the cathedral in Toledo (panel; fig. 1), in the National Museum of Warsaw (canvas), in the Galleria Nazionale Corsini in Rome (canvas) and there had been one (canvas) on the London market. While the first two are identical to the one here, even in size, the others, perhaps from the atelier, are slightly smaller (for all the versions see Rosci, 1999, pp. 36, 214-217 with bibliography). The three bigger paintings differ only in the rendering of the Samaritan's robes: here they are more fluid and transparent, while in the Toledo panel they seem to be modeled by constructive brushstrokes, and in the Warsaw canvas they are created with a thicker impasto and, in fact, some reservations have been voiced as to the authorship of this last painting (E. Arslan, *Una rettifica al catalogo della mostra del Cerano,* in "Arte lombarda", 10, 1965, p. 110).

When the painting shown here was not yet known, Rosci had proposed a dating around 1618-1620 for the Warsaw canvas (M. Rosci, *Mostra del Cerano,* Novara 1964, p. 99). Pérez Sànchez opted for circa 1630 for the Toledo version, and he noted a very close similarity between the Samaritan with her muscular arms and the servant in the Visitation from the *Mysteries of the Rosary* series in S. Maria al Vigentino, that had been published by Testori and considered datable around 1605 (A.E. Pérez Sànchez, *Pintura italiana del Siglo XVII en España,* Madrid 1965, p. 351).

James Byam Shaw, former director of the Colnaghi gallery, was the first scholar to note the existence of the Manchester panel and defined it as "much better" than the Warsaw version: this can be gleaned from a note on his copy of the catalogue from the 1964 exhibition in Novara which is conserved in the Colnaghi archives (Garstang, in *Master Paintings,* 1994, p. 38). Peter Cannon-Brookes was responsible for the first scientific publication of the painting, which in the meantime had been moved to

Fig 1. Cerano, *Christ and the Samaritan Woman at the Well,* Toledo, Cathedral.

Heythrop Park (Banbury); he reiterated its authenticity and proposed a very early dating, around the first decade of the seventeenth century, partly because of a misunderstanding of Perez Sànchez's writings and the relationship with the *Mysteries of the Rosary* (Cannon-Brookes, 1974, pp. 112-113). This hypothesis was accepted by Garstang (in *Master Paintings,* 1994, p. 41) who compared the painting to the four small panels on the Franciscan theme that are now divided between the Pinacoteca di Brera and the Pinacoteca del Castello Sforzesco in Milan, and are traditionally associated with the lost *Vow of Franciscan Saints* painted in 1600 (a link that Vito Zani has called into question with convincing arguments in M. Gregori (ed.), *Pittura a Milano dal Seicento al Neoclassicismo,* Cinisello Balsamo 1999, pp. 203-204).

Rosci continues to disagree with such a dating for the *Samaritan Woman.* He considers this the first and best version of the theme, a typical example of the painter's fully mature style that served as formal and iconographic inspiration for the young Daniele Crespi and for the subsequent works of Carlo Francesco Nuvolone. Therefore, it should be dated in the later years of the second decade; the indisputable relationship with the *Mysteries* should not interfere with this proposal since they should be considered later and non-autograph works (Rosci, 1984, p. 708; Idem,

1999, pp. 216-217). Even though there is no other proof, this hypothesis seems viable, particularly in light of the similarity to the *Beheading of Saint Denis* in Vigevano, that was certainly painted after 1616. The two paintings share the spectacular depth of the landscape illuminated by a cold gleam and enlivened by distant figures, the virtuoso rendering of the metals and, above all, the similar use of chiaroscuro in the figures of Christ and Saint Rusticus.

In the *Christ and the Samaritan Woman*, Rosci has recognized an iconographic module and theme that are characteristic of the devotional realism - with "commonplace" Biblical and Gospel scenes - of Carracci's Bolognese milieu, that later spread throughout the Lombard and Genoese areas; it is rich in "a new essence " with respect to the more sentimental models of his earlier years. To these references we must add the persistence of delicate Baroque echoes and a reference to Bassano in the compositional rhythm, in the lights and in the woman's astonished, almost incredulous expression. That Cerano's attention to Bassano's painting was more than sporadic is proved by a lost painting he did for Amedeo dal Pozzo, whose collection in 1634 included "the Samaritan from the Gospel parable, a copy of Bassano excellently done by Serrano" (A. Cifani-F. Monetti, *L'"illustrissimo cugino": Cassiano e Amedeo Dal Pozzo...*, exhibition catalogue (Biella), Rome 2001, p. 46, no. 193).

The hasty execution of the woman's robes and Christ's right hand that is barely roughed and contrasts with the other that has the almost macabre details of an X-ray, should perhaps be viewed as competing with the beauty Giulio Cesare Procaccini's successful drawings. In any case, this is a painting "where there is color, naturalness and grace born from the paintbrush, without effort, embellished with marvelous, picturesque and poetic decorations", as Giulio Mancini wrote around 1620 of the since lost *Saint Cecilia* that belonged to Cardinal Scaglia (G. Mancini, *Considerazioni sulla pittura*, 1617-1621 circa, ed. 1956-1957, 1, pp. 305-306). In addition to the number of versions, the success of this creation is further substantiated by the echo we see in Morazzone's canvas of the same subject that is now in the Pinacoteca di Brera and which Stoppa has attributed to the artist's studio (J. Stoppa, *Il Morazzone*, Milan 2003, p. 270). Although it portrays half-figures, and reveals most explicit Genoese influences, we see the identical gesture of Christ's hand, the texture and gleam of the copper basin, and above all

the ability to translate profound sentiments into gestures which Morazzone (or someone in his atelier) forces almost to the point of caricature.

The subject and the manner in which it is handled - and we can imagine that it satisfied the tastes of the shrewdest collectors - evoke an aspect of the artist's career that is somewhat overshadowed by the tendency to read the scenes almost exclusively in the key of torment-filled public devotions.

However, there was also another Cerano, as a famous passage by Borsier suggests - "owning drawings by Procaccino or by Cerano is something worthy of a prince..." which hints at a certain predilection for aristocratic milieus (L. Caramel, *Arte e artisti nell'epistolario di Girolamo Borsieri*, in "Contributi dell'istituto di storia dell'arte medievale e moderna", I, 1966, p. 136). Nor can we overlook Mancini's description ("of noble appearance and a fine horseman...") or the explicit words of Torre: "he lived as a noble, because of his birth or because he associated with princes" (C.Torre, *Il ritratto di Milano*, Milan 1674, pp. 10-11). The reference to noble origins suggests taking a closer look at the testimony published in 1628 by the influential Francsican Paolo Ferragallo Miglio, which has not been widely mentioned in studies on the artist: "Signor Gio. Battista Crespo, noble citizen of Milan, was also named for Cerano, since as a young man already excelling in painting, he would enjoy long holidays with his father, Raffaele, on the estates he owned in this delightful place and was nicknamed Cerano, and now that with age he has matured his art which is unsurpassed, and perhaps not even equaled either in Milano or beyond, this nickname has taken root among the people and so he signs his finest works as Gio Battista Cerano" (G. Garzoli, *Trecate. Storia delle chiese*, Trecate 1990, pp. 118-119). The expression "noble citizen" is not rhetorical and it is confirmed by the Crespi family's coat of arms that appears in the engraved portrait of the artist done by his son-in-law, Gherardino, after the painter died. An identical coat of arms is visible in the rug in the middle of the *Miracle of Beatrice Crespi* in the series dedicated to Saint Charles Borromeo; in another episode of that series Cerano did not hesitate to portray himself conversing with Renato Borromeo: perhaps a sign of a slight abundance of personal and noble interests that seeped into the celebrations of the new saint.

Federico Cavalieri

TIBERIO TITI
1573 - Florence - 1627

Portrait of Ferdinando Gonzaga, duke of Mantua. ca. 1617

Oil on canvas
83.5 x 49.2 in / 212 x 125 cm

This painting is a full-length portrait of a nobleman standing with his left hand on the hilt of his sword and the right hand resting on his waist. The nobleman has dark brown hair, a goatee and whiskers and is wearing a white ruff and a costly breastplate, with three black eagles on it. His outfit is completed by red hose and red breeches with silver embroidery, beige shoes with red laces and a red silk sash tied around his left arm. A heavy gold and enamel chain hangs from his neck. The sitter's helmet, decorated with red and white feathers, rests by his side on a table covered with forest green velvet. A matching green and mustard door-curtain appears on the other side of the figure.

A second version of this portrait, of slightly-lower quality, belongs to the Uffizi Gallery in Florence (Tiberio Titi, *Portrait of Ferdinando Gonzaga*, Florence, Uffizi Gallery, storage, 1890 inventory no. 2330, oil on canvas, 211 x 126 cm). Though one notes a few minor differences between the two paintings, for example in the folds of the velvet door-curtain and table-cloth and the position of the sitter's right hand, there can be little doubt that they portray the same sitter. The Uffizi version, currently in storage, was exhibited in the nineteenth century in the hallway suspended above the Ponte Vecchio that connects the gallery with the Pitti Palace. It was hanging in this hallway when the 1890 inventory of the gallery was compiled. In this inventory the sitter was first identified as the Marquis Vincenzo Gonzaga (*Inventario della Galleria degli Uffizi*, 1890, Florence, Soprintendenza per il Polo Museale Fiorentino, Research Department, register 4, p. 33, no. 2330). At an unspecified date Vincenzo's name was crossed out and substituted with the current identification of the sitter as Duke Ferdinando Gonzaga, duke of Mantua and of

Fig 1. Golden Scudo of Ferdinand Gonzaga, Duke of Mantua.

the Monferrato from 1613 to 1626.

Ferdinando Gonzaga (1587-1626), was the second of the four sons of Duke Vincenzo I Gonzaga and his wife Eleonora de' Medici. He was sent by his parents to the Universities of Ingolstadt and in Pisa, where he studied philosophy, theology and law as preparation for a career in the church. After becoming a clergyman, Ferdinando was first granted knighthood by the military order of Saint John of Jerusalem and in 1607 a cardinalate. In the meantime Ferdinando cultivated his passion for music and theatre and developed a taste for the fine arts. He led a costly, dissolute life that continued, unrestrained even after he became cardinal. His life-style changed radically when his older brother Francesco, duke of Mantua and of the Monferrato, died on the 22 December 1612. Since Francesco left no legitimate male heirs, Emperor Mattias designated Ferdinando as his successor on 21 October 1613. Ferdinando left the cloth in December of the same year and returned his cardinal's hat to Pope Paul V on 16 November 1615. He was officially crowned duke of Mantua and Monferrato on the 6 January 1616. Shortly afterwards Ferdinando staged a false wedding ceremony in order to seduce a young Monferrato noblewoman named Camilla Faà, who gave birth to a son named Giacinto on 4 December 1616. Undeterred by this relationship, on 12 February 1617 the duke married Caterina de' Medici (1593-1629), the daughter of Grand Duke Ferdinando I of Tuscany.

Ferdinando Gonzaga ruled in magnificent style, spending prodigal sums for patronage that compromised the already precarious finances of the duchy. Thus, shortly after his death on 29 October 1626, his younger brother and successor Vincenzo (1594-1627) found himself obliged to sell off much of the famous Gonzaga collection. In the meantime dense political clouds were accumulating over the duchy. Duke Charles Emanuel of Savoy's pressing claims on the Monferrato territory and Emperor Ferdinand II's displeasure over Vincenzo's chosen successor, the Frenchman Charles Gonzaga de Nevers, soon led to the imperial siege (1629) and sack (1630) of Mantua (For further biographical information concerning Ferdinando Gonzaga, see G. Benzoni, *Ferdinando Gonzaga, duca di Mantova e del Monferrato in the Dizionario biografico degli italiani*, Rome: Istituto della Enciclopedia Italiana fondata da Giovanni Treccani, 1960-[...], vol. 46, 1996, pp. 242-252; Giancarlo

Malacarne, *I Gonzaga di Mantova, una stirpe per una capitale europea*, vol. IV, *Splendore e Declino: da Vincenzo I a Vincenzo II (1587-1627)*, Modena: Il Bulino, 2007, pp. 237-249).

The identification with Ferdinando Gonzaga is convincing. The features of the sitter in this portrait and in the Uffizi replica closely resemble the ones impressed on a four scudi coin in gold bearing the inscription FERDIN D G DVX MANT VI / ET MONTIS FERRATI IV (Belfanti in *Monete e medaglie di Mantova* 1997, p. 260, no. 865; fig. 1). They are also similar to Ferdinando's features in a miniature portrait in Vienna's Kunsthistorisches Museum (Reproduced by Marco Belfanti in the chapter concerning Ferdinando Gonzaga in *Monete e medaglie di Mantova e dei Gonzaga dal XII al XIX Secolo* vol. IV, *I Gonzaga duchi di Mantova e marchesi poi duchi del Monferrato (1530-1627)*, Milan: Electa, 1997, p. 221) and in a bust-length portrait of the duke in a private collection bearing the inscription "FERDI. GONZ. DVC. MANT. ET M. FER." (Malacarne 2007, p. 245). In this last portrait Ferdinando is wearing the same heavy gold chain that appears in the present painting. The links of the chain are decorated with the words DOMINE and PROBASTI, taken from Psalm 138, and with burning crucibles, one of the Gonzaga heraldic emblems. Two angels bearing the holy reliquary with Christ's blood appear on the chain's pendant. We can thus recognize the gold chain as the insignia of the grand master of the military order founded by Ferdinando's father Vincenzo I Gonzaga, the knights of the "Redentore", or Redeemer, also known as the order of the "Preziosissimo Laterale Sangue di Cristo", literally of the Precious Blood of Christ's Flank (Malacarne 2007, pp. 140-153). Further confirmation is supplied by an inventory of the Pitti Palace compiled between 1663 and 1664 that lists a portrait of Duke Ferdinando of Mantua hanging in Prince Mattias de' Medici's apartment on the second floor of the palace (*Inventario di tutti i mobili che si ritrovano nel Palazzo de' Pitti di Sua Altezza Serenissima consegniati a Jacinto Maria Marmi, nuovo guardaroba entrato per morte di Biagio Marmi suo zio,* [...], 1663-1664, Florence, Archivio di Stato, Guardaroba medicea 725, folio 103 verso). It specifies that Duke Ferdinando rested his hand on his helmet, exactly the way he does in the portrait now in the Uffizi gallery: *'/216 Un Quadro in tela entrovi dipinto al naturale il Duca Ferdinando di Mantova che posa la mano sopra il morione con adornamento nero filettato d'oro alto braccia 4 e largo braccia 2 2/3'*.

Both the portrait of Ferdinando Gonzaga under discussion and the one in the Uffizi Gallery can be attributed to the Florentine portraitist Tiberio Titi, a son and follower of the well-known sixteenth century painter Santi di Tito. The brushwork, sharp lighting and format of the portrait remind us of a documented work of Tiberio's, his portrait of Ferdinando's wife, *Caterina de' Medici in white* (Tiberio Titi, *Caterina de' Medici in white, Florence,* Uffizi Gallery, 1890 inventory no. 2427, oil on canvas, 196 x 117 cm; fig. 2), also in the Uffizi Gallery. Her portrait, once considered a work of the Flemish Giusto Suttermans (Gaetano Pieraccini attributed the portrait of *Caterina de' Medici in white* to Giusto Suttermans (see La Stirpe de' Medici di Cafaggiolo, Florence: Vallecchi, 1924-1925, vol. II, 1925, pp. 438-439, pl. LXXV, fig. LXXX) and his attribution has been repeated by most scholars until quite recently. The portrait was in fact exhibited in 2002 as a work of Suttermans' (see the catalogue of the exhibition I *Volti del Potere. La ritrattistica di corte nella Firenze Granducale,* Florence, Uffizi, Sala delle Reali Poste, 30 May-28 July 2002, edited by Caterina Caneva, Florence: Giunti, 2002, pp. 72-74, no. 19). For the attribution to Tiberio Titi, see Lisa

Fig 2. Tiberio Titi, *Caterina de' Medici in white,* Florence, Uffizi Gallery.

Goldenberg Stoppato in *Il Seicento fiorentino. Arte a Firenze da Ferdinando I a Cosimo III,* catalogue of the exhibition (Florence, Palazzo Strozzi, 21 December 1986-4 May 1987), Florence: Cantini 1986, Pittura, p. 314, sub no. 1.160; Lisa Goldenberg Stoppato in *Pitture fiorentine del Seicento,* catalogue of the exhibition (Florence, Palazzo Ridolfi, 28 April- 31 May 1987), Turin: Allemandi, 1987, p. 104, sub no. 36; Costanza Contù, *Gusto e moda alla Corte medicea,* in I gioielli dei Medici dal vero e in ritratto, edited by Maria Sframeli, catalogue of the exhibition (Florence, Palazzo Pitti, Museo degli Argenti, 12 September 2003-2 February 2004), Livorno: Sillabe, 2003, pp. 50, 51, fig.), can easily be recognized as the full-length portrait of the Duchess that Tiberio Titi was working on the 20 April 1618, wrote a letter to Medici court secretary Andrea Cioli from the Gonzaga court (Letter from Tiberio Titi to Andrea Cioli, Mantua, 20 April 1618, Florence, Archivio di Stato, Mediceo del Principato 1376, unpaginated folio, published by Carlo Pini and Gaetano Milanesi, *La scrittura degli artisti italiani (sec. XIV-XVII) riprodotta con la fotografia,* Florence: Le Monnier, 1869-1876, vol. III, 1876, doc. 256). In the letter he specified that Duchess Caterina had posed for this portrait wearing the white dress she wore when she first arrived as a bride in Mantua: '*Havendomi dato intenzione la Signora Duchessa che fra 15 giorni, che sarà finito un suo Ritratto intero in abito biancho, come quando fece l'entrata in Mantova, darmi licenzia, però se Madama Serenissima [Christine de Lorraine] volendomi far gratia di comandarmi qualche cosa, me sarà singular favore […].*'

Further correspondence between the Medici and Gonzaga court makes it clear that Tiberio was sent to Mantua from Florence in January 1618 to paint a portrait of Eleonora Gonzaga, Duke Ferdinando's sister, who was sent to Vienna to facilitate the negotiations for her betrothal to the Emperor. The correspondence also mentions a portrait of Ferdinando's niece Maria Gonzaga that Tiberio painted while he was in Mantua (Isabelle Paulussen, *Tiberio Titi, ritrattista dei Medici,* in "Mededelingen van het Nederlands Instituut te Rome", (1980), pp. 107-108, 121, note 57; Lisa Goldenberg Stoppato, *A grand duchess and her painters as matchmakers: Maria Magdalena of Austria, Tiberio Titi, Giusto Suttermans and the betrothal of Empress Eleonora Gonzaga in Medici Power and Representation in Early Modern Europe,* currently in print).

None of the letters that document Tiberio Titi's visit to Mantua mention portraits of Ferdinando Gonzaga. It is thus possible that both the full-length portrait under discussion and the one in the Uffizi Gallery were painted in Florence in 1617, when Duke Ferdinando went to Tuscany to marry Caterina de' Medici. The sash with the initials CM embroidered on it, tied around the duke's arm in both portraits, lends weight to the hypothesis.

Archival research done in recent years has substantially emptied the catalogue raisonné of portraits referred to Tiberio Titi by Isabelle Paulussen in 1980 (Paulussen 1980, pp. 101-128) and by Simona Lecchini Giovannoni in 1986 (Simona Lecchini Giovannoni, in *Il Seicento fiorentino* 1986, *Biografie,* pp. 176-177, *Pittura,* p. 139, no. 1.37). The documentation discovered reattributes most of the portraits once thought to be works of Tiberio's to a variety of other painters, including his father Santi di Tito, Cristofano Allori, Jacopo Ligozzi, Domenico and Valore Casini, Francesco Bianchi Buonavita and Filippo Furini, better known as Pippo Sciameroni. These two portraits of *Duke Ferdinando Gonzaga* and the one of *Caterina de' Medici* in the Uffizi Gallery thus represent three rare, valid cornerstones for the reconstruction of a new catalogue of Tiberio's portraiture.

Lisa Goldenberg Stoppato

VALORE CASINI
1590 - Florence - 1660

Portrait of the actor Francesco Andreini, ca.1623

Oil on canvas
78.7 x 49.2 in / 200 x 125 cm

PROVENANCE
Rome, Lucien Bonaparte collection, room VI, 1808;
London, February 6, 1815, unsold at the first sale of Lucien Bonaparte collection;
London, May 14-16, 1816, sold at the second sale of the Lucien Bonaparte collection;
France, Baron H. de la Bouillerie collection;
Indre-et-Loire, Château de Villandry, Joachim Carvalho collection, 1925;
Lugano, private collection, 1953;
Paris, Hôtel des Ventes, sale of *Tableax anciens et modernes,* November 19, 1953, lot no. 91;
Koelliker collection.

EXHIBITIONS
Paris, Hôtel Jean Charpentier, *Exposition d'art ancien espagnol, organisée par la Demeure Historique,* June 6-July 6, 1925.

LITERATURE
G.A. Guattani, *Galleria del Senatore Luciano Bonaparte,* Roma 1808, vol. I, p. 111, no. 59;
Choix de gravures à l'eau-forte, d'après les peintures originales et les marbres de la galerie de Lucien Bonaparte - cent quarante-deux gravures, London 1812, p. 4, no. 82, pl. 82;
Catalogue of the Splendid Collection of Pictures belonging to Prince Lucien Bonaparte, which will be exhibited for sale by Private Contract, on Monday the Sixth Day of February, 1815 and following days, at the New Gallery, (Mr. Buchanans), [...], London 1815, p. 43, no. 158;
Magnificent Gallery of Paintings, catalogue of the sale, London, Stanley, May 14-16, 1816, London 1816, no. 86;
W. Buchanan, *Memoirs of Painting; with a Chronological History of the Importation of Pictures by the Great Masters into England since the French Revolution,* London, 1824, vol. II, p. 291, no. 112; J. Carvalho et al, *Exposition d'art ancien espagnol du 6 juin au 6 juillet 1925 en l'Hôtel Jean Charpentier Paris, organisée par la Demeure Historique,* Paris 1925, no. 108;
H. Olsen, *Federico Barocci,* Copenhagen 1962, p. 241;
E.A. Safarik, *Fetti,* Milano 1990, pp. 284-286 (fig.);
R. Bartoli Contini, *La Galleria Bonaparte. Catalogo,* in M. Natoli (editor), *Luciano Bonaparte le sue collezioni d'arte, le sue residenze a Roma, nel Lazio, in Italia (1804),* Rome 1995, p. 318-319, no. 13;
E.A. Safarik (editor), *Domenico Fetti (1588/89-1623),* catalogue of the exhibition (Mantua, Palazzo Tè, September 15-December 15, 1996), Milano 1996, p. 181, sub no. 43;

S. Ferrone, *Pose sceniche di una famiglia d'attori* in E.A. Safarik (a cura di), *Domenico Fetti (1588/89-1623),* 1996, p. 52, fig. 2;
S. Mazzoni, *Genealogia e vicende della famiglia Andreini,* in *Origini della Commedia. Improvvisa o dell'arte,* proceedings of the seminar (Rome and Anagni October 12-15, 1995), Rome 1996, p. 119;
B. Edelein-Badie, *La collection de tableaux de Lucien Bonaparte, prince de Canino,* Paris 1997, p. 148, no. 11;
M. Gregori, "Due ritrattisti fiorentini da tenere in considerazione: Valore e Domenico Casini", in *Gazette des beaux-arts,* no. 135, 2000, pp. 135-137, fig. 7;
L. Goldenberg Stoppato, "Per Domenico e Valore Casini, ritrattisti fiorentini", in *Mitteilungen des Kunsthistorischen Institutes in Florenz,* 48, 2004 (2005), p. 198, note 40;
Teatro italiano tra letteratura, commedia dell'arte, feste e melodramma (XVI-XVIII sec.), Lugano/ Rozzano 2005, reproduced on the cover;
F. Petrucci, *Bernini pittore "dal disegno al meraviglioso composto",* Rome 2006, p. 399, fig. 8a.

This full-length portrait comes from the Roman collection of Prince Lucien Bonaparte: it is listed in Giuseppe Antonio Guattani's 1808 catalogue of the *Galleria del Senatore Luciano Bonaparte.* An etched reproduction of the portrait by Filippo Pistrucci was published in 1812 in the volume of etchings after selected paintings from the same gallery. When the Bonaparte collection was presented for sale in London in 1815 by William Buchanan, this painting was not sold. It was represented for sale in London by George Stanley the following year, along with other works from the collection. According to the annotated copy of the 1816 sale catalogue consulted by Béatrice Edelein-Badie, it was sold for 32 pounds and 11 shillings. Professor Mina Gregori (2000) suggested, without mentioning her source of information, an earlier provenance from the collection of the Marquis del Carpio Gaspar de Haro y Guzman (1629-1687), who came to Italy as the Spanish ambassador to the Holy See and was later named Viceroy of Naples. Unfortunately, the portrait does not seem to appear in the inventories of the marquis' collection published by Marcus Burke and Peter Cherry (see *Spanish Inventories 1. Collections of Paintings in Madrid 1601-1755,* Malibu 1997, pp. 726-786, 815-828).

The Bonaparte catalogues identify the sitter

Fig 1. Domenico Fetti, *Portrait of Francesco Andreini holding a Mask,* Saint Petersburg, Hermitage.

in this portrait as the "Tyrant Cavalca" from Pesaro. This identification was set aside by both of the modern authors who have studied the collection of Lucien Bonaparte, Béatrice Edelein-Badie and Roberta Bartoli Contini. The sitter's true identity was established in 1990 by Eduard Safarik, while he was examining Domenico Fetti's portrait of an actor holding a mask that belongs to Saint Petersburg's Hermitage (fig. 1). As Safarik pointed out, when the Fetti portrait was reproduced in 1742, it was clearly indicated as the portrait of a 'Comedien', a commedia dell'arte actor, who worked for the Duke of Mantua (see *Recueil d'estampes d'après les plus beaux tableaux et d'après les plus beaux desseins qui sont en France dans le cabinet du Roy, dans celui de Monseigneur le Duc d'Orléans, et dans d'autres cabinets [...],* Paris, 1729-1742, vol. II, 1742, p. 40, pl. 109). Safarik discarded a series of names of actors that had previously been suggested for the sitter and identified the sitter in Fetti's portrait as Francesco Andreini, the Tuscan 'comico' who invented the character Capitan Spavento, literally Captain Fear, from Vall'Onferno. As Safarik pointed out, the features of Fetti's actor perfectly match those of *Francesco Andreini* in a engraving by Abraham Tummermann, which was first published in Andreini's Le Bravure del *Capitano Spavento* (Venice: Giacomo Antonio Somasco, 1609). Safarik recognized the same features in the so-called portrait of 'Tyrant Calvaca' from the Lucien Bonaparte collection, which he knew

thanks to a Giraudon photograph (Paris, G 16688-9), taken when the painting belonged to the Carvalho collection at Villandry. The theatrical gesture of the sitter in this full-length portrait makes perfect sense for an actor.

Francesco Andreini, (ca. 1544 – 1624), born in Pistoia in the mid 1540's, married the famous actress and poet Isabella Canali around 1575. Together they founded a *commedia dell'arte* troupe known as the *Compagnia dei Gelosi*. The Gelosi reached great acclaim in 1589 at the festivities for the wedding of Ferdinando I de' Medici and Christine de Lorraine and, over the years, gained the patronage of the courts of Mantua and Paris as well. A frescoed lunette in the cloister of the Florentine convent of the Santissima Annunziata gives us a measure of the Andreini's status in Florence: Francesco, Isabella and their son Giovanni Battista appear in prominent positions in this frescoed depiction of *The Servite Sostegno at the court of France,* painted by Bernardino Barbatelli, known as il Poccetti, for the Usimbardi family. Francesco retired as an actor in 1604, after the Isabella's sudden death, and dedicated his energies to publishing first his wife's and then his own works. He settled in Mantua, where he was granted citizenship in 1607 and died on August 20, 1624 (for further biographical information on Francesco Andreini, see F. Angelini Frajese in Dizionario *Biografico degli Italiani,* Rome 1969-[...], vol. 3, 1961, pp. 132-133; S. Ferrone (ed.), *Comici dell'Arte. Corrispondenze G.B. Andreini, N. Barbieri, P. M. Cecchini, S. Fiorillo, T. Martinelli, F. Scala,* Florence 1993, vol. I, pp. 97-98, note 97; S. Mazzoni 1996 (cited above), pp. 107-121; S. Ferrone 1996 (cited above), pp. 51-53; A. MacNeil, *Music and Women of the Commedia dell'Arte in the Late Sixteenth Century,* Oxford, 2003, pp. 46-50).

All of the Bonaparte collection and sale catalogues attributed this portrait to the famous painter from Urbino, Federico Barocci. Harald Olsen dismissed this attribution as quite "unlikely" in his 1962 monograph, judging simply from the etched reproduction of the portrait, which he listed among Barocci's lost works. The portrait had in fact resurfaced in the meantime with an equally improbable attribution to Diego Velázquez: it was exhibited as a portrait of the Marquis Spinola by Velázquez at the Hôtel Jean Charpentier in 1925, when it belonged to the collection of Joaquim Carvalho in the Château de Villandry, and was sold at auction with the same attribution in 1953. Eduard Safarik proposed a tentative attribution

to Giusto Suttermans, the Flemish portraitist of the Medici court in Florence, which was repeated in the catalogue of the 1996 Fetti exhibition and in 2006 by Francesco Petrucci. Roberta Bartoli's catalogue of the works once in the Bonaparte gallery (1995), prudently attributed this portrait to an unspecified Florentine painter close to Jacopo da Empoli. In 2000 Mina Gregori proposed the names of the Florentine portraitists Domenico and Valore Casini, who were born respectively in 1588 and 1590 and both died in 1660.

The Casini brothers are mentioned only briefly in Filippo Baldinucci's Notizie de' *professori del disegno [...]* (1681-1728, edited by F. Ranalli, 1845-1847, vol. III, 1846, pp. 450-451) as pupils of Domenico Cresti known as il Passignano. Baldinucci singles out Valore for praise as a "uomo di valore", literally a man of value, capable of painting candid, close resemblances. Since Baldinucci indicates that Domenico's only painted the sitter's clothing, it is clear that he played a secondary role in the artistic partnership with his younger brother. The portrait of *Francesco Andreini* is of notably better quality than much of the work produced by the Casini brothers, a consideration that at first glance might raise questions about the attribution (see Goldenberg Stoppato, 2004). However, after careful consideration, one can find comparable, excellent brushwork in the few portraits that Valore Casini painted by himself, without Domenico's help. A good example is the portrait of *Niccolò Pesciolini (1535-1619),* once in the Nomi-Pesciolini collection in San Gimignano, which bears an old inscription with Valore's name on the back of the canvas (Goldenberg Stoppato, 2004, pp. 167-168, 197, note 35, fig. 3). In both cases one notes under the flesh tones the same, dark underpainting, a technique he may well have learned from Passignano.

The portrait of *Francesco Andreini* can also be compared to an extremely interesting canvas that portrays a ball player, a work recently rediscovered in storage in Palazzo Pitti (1890 Inv. no. 5292, kindly called to my attention as a possible Suttermans by Dr. Fausta Navarro). This canvas matches perfectly with the description of a portrait of *"Mochone maestro di palla a corda,* alto 3 ½, largo 2 ½" listed without an attribution in a palace register in 1638. The same full-length portrait appears in the Casini brother's accounting book: this manuscript mentions a "ritrato di Mochone intero" delivered to Grand Duke Cosimo II on September 16, 1619.

The full-length portrait of Francesco Andreini was probably painted by Valore Casini a few years later. Eduard Safarik dates his portrait by Domenico Fetti in the Hermitage before June 1620, when Andreini left Mantua and traveled to Milan and France with his son Giovan Battista's Compagnia de' Fedeli. Though the troupe returned to Italy for a few months in 1622, Andreini seems to have made his definitive return to Mantua in April 1623, well after Fetti left for Venice for the last time (see S. Ferrone, 1996, p. 58, note 4). Since Francesco Andreini appears to be several years older in the portrait by Valore Casini, it must have been painted fairly close to the date of the actor's death, possibly, if the actor travelled by ship from Marseilles to Livorno, during a stop in Florence on his trip back to Mantua.

Lisa Goldenberg Stoppato

GIOVAN BATTISTA CARACCIOLO CALLED BATTISTELLO CARACCIOLO
1578 - Naples - 1635

Christ preaching to the Disciples, 1628 - 1635

Oil on canvas
50.4 x 60.6 in / 128 x 154 cm

PROVENANCE
Genoa, Doria collection;
Brussels, Arenberg collection;
Germany, Private collection.

EXHIBITIONS
Sidney-Melbourne, *Caravaggio & His World*,
2003-2004, no. 20;
Milan-Vienna, *Caravaggio e l'Europa. Il
movimento caravaggesco internazionale da
Caravaggio a Mattia Preti,* no. VI.11 8;
Ariccia, Palazzo Chigi, *La "Schola" del
Caravaggio. Dipinti della collezione Koelliker,*
13 October 2006 - 11 February 2007, no. 88;
Naples, Museo di Capodimonte, *Ritorno
al Barocco. Da Caravaggio a Vanvitelli,* 12
December - 11 April 2010, no. 1.2.

LITERATURE
F. Bologna, in *Fifty Paintings 1535-1825,*
exhibition catalogue (Matthiesen Gallery,
London-New York), 1993, no. 12;
Mattia Preti tra Roma, Napoli e Malta, catalogo
della mostra, Napoli 1999, p. 17;
S. Causa, *Battistello Caracciolo. L'opera
completa,* Napoli 2000, no. A103;
An Art Odyssey, catalogo della mostra
(Matthiesen Gallery, London), 2001, no. 27;
J. Spike, in *Caravaggio & His World,* exhibition
catalogue, Sidney-Melbourne 2003, no. 20;
W. Prohaska, in *Caravaggio e l'Europa. Il
movimento caravaggesco internazionale da
Caravaggio a Mattia Preti,* exhibition catalogue,
Milan 2005, no. VI.11 8;
G. Papi (ed.), in *La "Schola" del Caravaggio.
Dipinti della collezione Koelliker,* exhibition
catalogue, Milan 2006, pp. 286-289;
W. Prohaska, in N. Spinosa (ed.), *Ritorno al
Barocco. Da Caravaggio a Vanvitelli,* exhibition
catalogue, Naples 2009, p. 63.

The traditional iconographic identification
of this painting - *The Calling of Saint Matthew*
- had already been called into question by
Bologna (1993), and then, at the exhibition
held in Milan in 2005 it was replaced by the
title used here. The "protagonist" of the scene
is clearly the money - in the pouch that the
apostle on the right is holding with a somewhat
embarrassed expression - and in clear view
on the table. The young apostle seems about
to count the coins while he turns towards
Christ whose gesture is unequivocally clear and
rhetorical - he is not pointing to a person as we
always see in the paintings of *The Calling of
Saint Matthew*.

There are several passages in the Gospels
according to Matthew and Luke in which
Christ draws attention to the negative effects
of money and riches that block the way to a
life of grace (see for example Matthew 10:5 ff.,
in which Christ instructs the apostles on their
mission and urges them to a life of poverty and
simplicity; cf. also Luke 6: 24 and Luke 12:33
ff.). In 2006, Papi, who agrees in part with this
author's doubts, used the traditional title *The
Calling of Saint Matthew,* but followed it with
a question mark.

Even following the publication of Stefano
Causa's monograph there are still many open
questions concerning the dating of Carraciolo's
work and some very important paintings such
as the frescoes in the Palazzo Reale in Naples are
still the subject of debate from the chronological
standpoint. Spinosa, too, has recently taken a
stand on this issue (2001, passim; cf. our entry
in the 2005 Milan exhibition catalogue, p.
424). If we exclude a payment made in 1611
which, in any case would be difficult to relate
to the conserved frescoes, we do not have any
documented point of reference for the Palazzo
Reale frescoes (the dates in the literature
oscillate between 1611 and the first half of the
1630s: Causa 2000, A23; cf. also Spinosa 2001,
p. 430). As to the chapels of the Certosa di San
Martino, we must consider that Caraccio lo,
ignoring the contractual agreements, took his
time after he finished the *Washing of the Feet*
(1622) in the choir of the Certosa, and left
behind the completion of the *"cappella difora
a frisco"* - clearly the frescoes in the chapel of
the Madonna were outside the choir - which
means that the frescoes in the Marian chapel
were probably only finished in the second half
of the 1620s.

Regarding the painting discussed here, Spike
has proposed a dating between 1625 (!) and
1635, the year of Caracciolo's death. We
would like to call attention to the relationship
with the *Madonna and Child with Saint Anne,*
conser ved in the Kunsthistorische Museum in
Vienna (fig. 1), which is generally considered a
later work, post 1630, even though it has not
been dated with any certainty. This painting,
too, is characterized by monumental figures,
clothed in full, flowing robes, which stand out
against the unreal architecture behind them, in
a space that is only defined by the plasticity of
the figures themselves.

Perhaps the similarity between the
monumental figures and draperies, poses and
expressions - notwithstanding the different
pictorial "touch" - of the two apostles in the
Apostolado by Ribera, in the Museo del Prado

Fig 1. Battistello Caracciolo, *Madonna and Child with Saint
Anne,* Vienna, Kunsthistorische Museum.

dating from the early 1630s (Spinosa 2003,
nos. A84, A87), and the features of the apostle
in the background on the left in Caracciolo's
painting can help us establish a timeframe.
According to Longhi, the "breath of *Riberism*"
also struck Caracciolo, albeit as an exception
(cf. R. Longhi, *Battistello,* in "L'Arte", XVIII,
1915). But it may also have been the other way
around, i.e. that in addition to being influenced
by the strong plasticity of the portraits of the
apostles Rubens painted in the early years of
the second decade, Ribera was inspired by
majesty of Caracciolo's figures that became
increasingly evident starting around 1628-30.
Papi (2006) speaks of an even earlier dating,
closer to the *Washing of the Feet* done in 1622.

Wolfgang Prohaska

ARTEMISIA GENTILESCHI
Rome 1593 - after January 1654 Naples

Portrait of an Unidentified Man, 1630 - 1640

Oil on canvas
80.5 x 43 in / 204.5 x 109.2 cm
Monogrammed AG on the silver trinkets.

Fig 2. Artemisia Gentileschi, *Portrait of a Woman with a Fan*, Genoa, private collection.

Artemisia Gentileschi is best-known for her powerful interpretations of Old Testament heroines such as Susanna and Judith. Early biographies, however, indicate that she was renowned for her portraiture, although scholars have not necessarily embraced this aspect of the artist's painted oeuvre. This is due in part to the rejection of the notion that Artemisia would have conformed to the stereotypical biography for women artists who typically excelled in non-narrative imagery such as still-life and portraiture. This reluctance to acknowledge Artemisia's skills as a portraitist is a product of the overwhelmingly feminist analysis that has governed much of Artemisia studies. There is no reason to reject the idea that Artemisia could and did provide accomplished portraits for her clients, as the already well-known Portrait of a *Gonfaloniere* (Palazzo d'Accursio, Bologna, Fig. 1) and the recently-discovered *Portrait of a Woman with a Fan* (Private Collection, Genoa, Fig. 2) easily attest. The present example of a full-scale male subject joins the small group of autograph Artemisia portraits and confirms the artist's considerable talents in the art of portraiture.

This painting portrays a well-dressed nobleman fashionably attired in a slashed doublet with paned (slashed) sleeves, breeches, and lace collar and cuffs. He certainly appears flamboyant and his dress comes remarkably close to one portrayed in Abraham Bosse's famous etching illustrating the effects of the 1633 French edict restricting elaborate costume to the upper classes (Figure 3). The outfit laid out on the chair (about to be removed by the servant) includes paned sleeves, lace cuffs, and decorative ribbons along the bottoms of the pants legs, the latter recalling the metal points (called aiguillettes) that decorate the fitted cuffs of our subject.

The high level of sartorial adornment is in keeping with the demeanor of Artemisia's subject. He holds his proper left hand at the hilt of his sword, extending his index finger, thereby connoting an individual of stature and confidence. His proper right arm juts aggressively and assuredly out from his hip, a pose of male aggression that was first identified and discussed by Joaneath Spicer in her 1991 essay, "The Renaissance Elbow." In fact, his proper right hand is turned completely in towards his body and recalls a passage in John Bulwer's *Chironomia,* his 1644 manual on using gesture in public speaking. The author disparages this very gesture: "to set the arms agambo or aprank, and to rest the turned-in back of the hand upon the side is an action of pride and ostentation, unbeseeming the hand of an orator." It seems, therefore, that this pose would have been understood by contemporaries as one of arrogance and pride.

There is no question that the painting is by Artemisia Gentileschi. One has only to compare this portrait to the 1622 *Portrait of a Gonfaloniere* (Fig. 1) to see that there are close similarities in pose, treatment of fabrics, hands, and the general placement and conception of the composition. The handling of the white fabric of the chemise that is rendered in crisp yet fluid strokes, the touch displayed on the definition of the slashed panels in the doublet, and the manner in which the hair has been painted conform not only to the portrait of the Gonfaloniere, but recall similar passages in Artemisia's paintings from the 1620s and 1630s. Elements of physiognomy also comply with the artist's output during these years, most evident in the wide flat forehead and the division of shading along the central axis of the face.

Beyond mere elements of style, the approach to male portraiture suggests the mind of Artemisia Gentileschi. When she painted the Gonfaloniere in 1622, she responded to the overwhelmingly macho bearing that had become typical of male portraiture from

Fig 1. Artemisia Gentileschi, *Portrait of a Gonfaloniere*, Bologne, Palazzo d'Accursio.

the time of Titian. Artemisia replaced the authoritative right hand that typically rested on canes, pointed to armorial elements, or grasped objects of ownership or rule with one tentatively poised on the corner of the nearby table, obviously eschewing any suggestion of aggression or command. In the current picture, she has gone in the other direction by including an overly assertive gesture and a more secure open stance, most likely in an attempt to provide insight into the character of her subject. One often senses in the work of Artemisia a decision to either deny established protocols or to create ones of her own.

One particularly "Artemisian" detail is the use of her initials in the silver trinkets worn around the sitter's neck. While she was not the only artist to use signatures as a gloss on narratives or as enhancements for subjects, Artemisia was certainly among the most creative picture signers. She experimented with diverse types and locations for signing her name. Her signatures appeared chiseled in stone, embroidered on upholstery, carved into a tree, signed on discarded paper, inscribed in a book, and worked into a metal shield. It is therefore not at all surprising to see her working her identifying initials into items of adornment worn by the subject. This suggests that she and the sitter were on intimate terms, but until an identity is discovered, it is not possible to confirm a relationship.

Determining the portrait's precise date is

a bit more difficult. Details of the costume certainly place the painting within the period between 1625 and 1640. The close analogy of the costume to Bosse's 1633 print confirms that window of time. Furthermore, lace became an extraordinarily popular costume adornment during the 1620s, and continued so in the subsequent decades, although exact identification of the lace is difficult. It could be a type of Venetian cut lace, known as *reticella*. However, the first half of the seventeenth century was a period in which many techniques were emerging, and needle and bobbin laces also became fashionable. Furthermore, the determination of dating and geography through clothing is made more complicated by the fact that many European centers followed identical fashion tastes and some styles lingered on in some locales and were abandoned in others, depending on personal preference and patterns of trade.

Stylistically, the picture should be placed in Artemisia's Neapolitan period, prior to 1640. The more refined shading of the face suggests that the picture may have been produced in the 1630s rather than the 1620s. The handling of light and shadow, particularly the more pronounced *sfumato,* ties the picture to Artemisia's work in Naples. Furthermore, the physiognomy relates closely to the heads found in some of her paintings of the mid-1630s, namely the *Birth of St. John the Baptist* and the *Corisca and the Satyr*.

The sitter's identity, at this point, remains unknown. Although the sitter appears to be Hispanic, such an identification is not certain. Given Artemisia's dealings with the Duc d'Alcalà first in Rome (he bought three pictures from her when he was the Spanish Ambassador to the Papacy in the mid 1620s) and then potentially in Venice and Naples (he visited Venice during the late 1620s before assuming his post as Spanish Viceroy in Naples in 1629), the possible identification of the sitter as someone within Alcalà's circle is not out of the question.

Judith W. Mann

Fig 3. Abraham Bosse, *Costume of Upper Classes,* engraving.

ANGELO CAROSELLI
1585 - Rome - 1652

Virgin and Child with Saint Anne, 1635 - 1645

Oil on panel
19.1 x 14.8 in / 48.5 x 37.7 cm

PROVENANCE
Rome, Sestieri collection;
Koelliker collection.

EXHIBITIONS
Ariccia, Palazzo Chigi, *La "schola" del Caravaggio. Dipinti dalla Collezione Koelliker*, 13 October 2006 - 11 February 2007, no. 41.

LITERATURE
A. Ottani Cavina, *Su Angelo Caroselli, pittore romano*, in "Arte antica e moderna", 31-32, 1965, p. 292, fig. 117a;
G. Papi (ed.), *La "schola" del Caravaggio. Dipinti dalla Collezione Koelliker*, exhibition catalogue, Milan 2006, pp. 154-55.

Anna Ottani published this painting with the correct attribution to Caroselli in her pioneering essay on the Roman artist. She presented it with an ample group of paintings of similar subjects, that included the *Madonna and Child with the Infant Baptist* of the City Art Gallery in Manchester (a picture that is particularly similar to the one shown here; fig. 1), the *Madonna and Child* in the Galleria Corsini, Rome and the *Madonna and Child* that had been in the Meissner Collection in Zurich. She also justly understood the artist's irrepressible archaizing intentions that are evident in the choice of the support (wood) and in the quasi-Renaissance presentation of the scene (the most striking example is certainly the *Virgin Enthroned with Angels Gabriel and Raphael* in the Uffizi, where we

Fig 2. Angelo Caroselli, *Virgin and Child with Saint Lawrence and Saint Stephen*, Baltimora, Baltimore Museum.

stylistically similar to our painting) *Virgin and Child with Saint Lawrence and Saint Stephen,* in the Baltimore Museum (fig. 2) which Federico Zeri had already attributed to Caroselli does not shed sufficient light on the many problems surrounding the artist including this specific painting that makes him a sort of ante *litteram Sassoferrato.*

Chronology is always a problem with Caroselli because his works are rarely, if ever, dated. Stefano Salerno suggests a dating with the Madonnas at the end of the third and during the fourth decades, and even though she does not deal specifically with time issues, Anna Ottani seems to advance a similar hypothesis.

Gianni Papi

should most probably perceive the intent to produce a forgery since his biographers all concur as to Caroselli's exceptional talent as an imitator). In this painting Ottani noted a sort of hiatus in the artist's development, as if he were stuck in a dry, dead-end: "Stubbornly grinding out the same thoughts, the artist later tended to translate them into a form that gradually became more flowing, if I am not mistaken in seeing in his creamy and fraying style, the signs of a contrived course, that progressively became stripped of any correspondence with the avant-garde of contemporary painting".

More than forty years have passed since that essay was published, and there is still no systematic and updated study of this complicated artist who was probably more important than acknowledged up to now. Thus, even this rich style (the quality of our painting is worthy of a miniaturist; the liveliness of the colors is astounding), the mysterious atmosphere of revival that we see in works such as this panel only serve to enhance the complex, multifaceted and to a large extent still obscure personality of this man, who lived through half of the seventeenth century and was in contact with the greatest artists of his day from Caravaggio, to Lanfranco, to Tassi. The recent essay by Stefano Salerno (Cf. S. Salerno, *Precisazioni su Angelo Caroselli,* in "Storia dell'arte", 76, 1992) publishing the remarkable (and

Fig 1. Angelo Caroselli, *Madonna and Child with the Infant Baptist*, Manchester, City Art Gallery.

LUCA GIORDANO
1634 - Naples - 1705

Philosopher with book and compass, 1655 - 1660

Oil on canvas
47 x 37.6 in / 119.5 x 95.5 cm

Provenance
Switzerland, Private collection.

The present painting can be associated with the renewal of a traditional humanistic theme which had an immense success in Italy, in France and in Holland in the seventeenth century. The most impressive examples are the riberesque models. On the basis of the portraits handed down from the Greek and Roman sculptures, from the antique literary sources such as the *Vitae* of Diogene Laerzio and from engravings, there were widespread iconographic repertories of wise persons and antique philosophers. Around them artists created numerous serial combinations, since there was no fixed "code" for reference. Often predestined to illustrate the different sections of a library, these series were formed around some key figures, socially characterised as ragged and begging philosophers, around which each time there different aggregations made, depending on the client and on the final destination.

In the series by Giordano, among the philosophers (understood in the more general sense) there are mathematicians, astrologers, astronomers, geographers and chemists, scientists, not easy to identify but recognizable by the attributes depicted which indicate their activity (see for example Fig 1).

The present picture, from the youth of the painter - between the end of the fifties and the beginning of the sixties of the Seventeenth century - represents a bearded man with a wide mantle which leaves unadorned his entire left shoulder. The right hand, which leans on an open book, holds a compass; the left shows a folded paper sheet with some geometric figures inscribed. The fine tones, all between the white, the ochre and the brown, the restrained pictorial treatment, the marked physiognomic characterisation but not yet driven to deformation and to an exasperated expressionism, brings the subject very close to the second group of *Philosophers* executed by Giordano when, critically assessing Ribera's *oeuvre,* he turns to the examples of high pictorial intensity of the Spanish master, which are to be dated at the middle of the thirties.

The severe and intense man, who emerges with vigorous and strong luminosity from the shadows of the background, where on the left you can catch a glimpse of some volumes placed on a shelf, is not easy to be identified for lack of precise attributes. Only a sign marked out on a cartouche might let us suppose him a mathematician or an astrologer. However, benefiting from a large margin of freedom in their creativity artists often produced hybrid and personalized types.

Giordano caught the trend of the philosophical culture of that time, characterised by the new stoic currents introduced by the close Roman environment between the end of the twenties and the beginning of the thirties. He achieved a high degree of intensity in the representation of such figures, highlighting their psychological and intellectual qualities through an investigation of the character often bordering on the grotesque. This underlines the contemporary influence of Giovanni Battista della Porta in his treaty *De Humana Physiognonomia,* which was hugely popular at the time.

The canvas would have been part of a series, whose reconstruction is today impossible, since these collections were lost over the course of time. There is another version of this painting with some slight variations, such as un-readable writing instead of the sign on the paper held in the philosopher's hand and a trace of words on the rolled up paper, formerly in a private Italian collection and sold at Christie's Rome the 15th of October 1970, no. 83 (See O. Ferrari-G. Scavizzi , *Luca Giodano,* Napoli 1992, vol. I, p. 27, n. A134 and vol. II, p. 538, ill. 217).

Fig 1. Luca Giordano, *Philosopher*, Munich, Alte Pinakothek.

Denise Maria Pagano

CARLO DOLCI
1616 - Florence - 1686

Saint Apollonia, ca. 1670s

Oil on canvas
25.2 x 20.3 in / 64 x 51.5 cm

PROVENANCE

Shropshire, Oakley Park, Robert Clive ('Clive of India'), 1st Baron Clive of Plassey (1725-1774); then by inheritance to the first son, Edward Clive, second Lord, 1st Earl of Powis; then by inheritance to the second son Robert Henry Clive (1789-1854), who married Harriet Windsor, daughter of the 5th Earl of Plymouth, Baroness Windsor;
Robert Windsor-Clive (1824-1859);
Robert George Windsor-Clive, 1st Earl di Plymouth (1857-1923); then by inheritance;
Milan, Koelliker collection.

LITERATURE

F. Leach (ed.), *The Country Seats of Shropshire,* Shrewsbury 1891, p. 212, ["St. Apollonia, by Carlo Dolce"];
G. Cantelli, *Repertorio della pittura fiorentina del Seicento,* Fiesole 1983, p. 72;
M. Chiarini (ed.), in *Bellezze di Firenze. Disegni fiorentini del Seicento e del Settecento dal Museo di Belle Arti di Lille,* exhibition catalogue, Florence 1991, p. 68, cat. n. 29;
F. Baldassari, *Carlo Dolci,* Turin 1995, pp. 115-116, fig. 85; F. Baldassari, in M. Gregori (ed.), *Pittura fiorentina XVII secolo.* Collezione Koelliker, Turin, pp. 16-17, 44.

The painting depicts Saint Apollonia, a deaconess who was martyred for not renoucing her faith during the persecution of the Christians under Emperor Philip the Arabian in 249 AD. During a festival held in Alexandria to commemorate the millennium of the founding of Rome, the Christians were dragged out of their houses and killed. Apollonia was attacked and had all her teeth pulled out and jaw broken by a group of the rampaging Alexandrians. She was then taken out of the city, threatened with being burnt alive, and ordered to recite blasphemous phrases renouncing her god. Asking for a moment of reflection, her captors loosening their grip, Apollonia jumped forward and threw herself into the flames.

Dolci has dedicated at least three autograph version in differing formats though similar measurements to this subject. Other versions include one housed in the Galleria Corsini in Rome, though on a hexagonal canvas, and an oval canvas belonging to a private Florentine collection. In all three the saint is depicted at half bust and dressed elegantly, clasping her breast with her right hand and holding in her left hand the tongs that brought about her martyrdom. Any allusion to the brutality of her torture is avoided by Dolci, who instead prefers to concentrate on the beauty of the subject, whose face is depicted with porcelain colours and illuminated by a heavenly light returning her stare.

The sublime technique of the artist is evident in every fold of the white lace that adorns the top of her red dress, in the reflections of light on the tongs and the palm of her hand and the soft lines of her face, her eyes gazing upwards as if to invoke faith and dispell fear as she becomes a martyr.

The image, intense in its treatment of emotional values, reveals stylistic characteristics of Dolci's more mature period, of the 1670s. The typological affinity and more stringent style place the work with definitively dated works such as *Charity* at the Cariprato at Prato (1659-1665; fig. 1) and the *Saint Barbara* (1667) in a private collection. The positioning of the hands of the saint was studied by Dolci in a drawing kept in the Musée des Beaux Art in Lille (Pl. 205, red chalk on white paper, 281 x 189 mm). The present painting however has a closer affinity with the aforementioned oval version in private hands - which shows the saint at three quarter length.

Francesca Baldassari

Fig 1. Carlo Dolci, *The Charity,* Prato, Cariprato Foudation.

GIACOMO CERUTI
1698 - Milan - 1767

The Brawl, 1720 - 1725

Oil on canvas
53.7 x 68.5 in / 136.5 x 174 cm

PROVENANCE
Vienna, private collection;
England, art market.

EXHIBITIONS
Parma, Galleria Nazionale, *Luce sul Settecento: Gaspare Traversi e l'arte del suo tempo in Emilia,* 4 April - 4 July 2004, no. 46.

LITERATURE
A. Loda, in L. Fornari Schianchi-N. Spinosa (ed.), *Luce sul Settecento. Gaspare Traversi e l'arte del suo tempo in Emilia,* exhibition catalogue (Parma), Naples 2004, p. 148, no. 46 (ill.).

Set in a dark interior with just a single source of light coming from the left, the painting depicts a violent fight between two relatively young men. The standing figure is grasping the kneeling man's hair with his left hand and is pointing his pistol at him, ready to fire, with his thumb raising the hammer. In response to the assault, the second figure - who has a gun in his tailcoat pocket - holds a knife to his rival's chest, but the other man's dog bites him, effectively thwarting his counterattack. Although their clothing would identify the two adversaries as members of the middle class, we must not ignore the untidy hair, the kneeling man's earring and the torn sleeve of his jacket that speak to the dissolute lifestyles of both figures.

Traditionally attributed to Giacomo Ceruti (as per a nineteenth century label on the back of the stretcher, indicating that it was in Vienna and identifying it as: "Italienische schüle. J. Ceruti gennant Pitocheto"), this author recognized the canvas (oral communication to the owners) about ten years ago as an example of the early years of the Milanese painter's career. Later, the painting was shown with the same attribution at the exhibition on Gaspare Traversi held in Parma in 2004, with a catalogue entry by Angelo Loda who emphasized the relationship with the artist's earlier works in Brescia and specifically the paintings from the Padernello cycle.

The reference to Ceruti is justified in the first place by the way the scene is framed and in the resulting compositional and spatial arrangements. As Loda has already noted, the choice of a raised and very close viewpoint (the scene seems to "slide" downwards on the floor) is a feature common to most of the artist's early genre scenes in which - just as in this painting - this expedient serves to

Fig 1. Giacomo Ceruti, *Cobblers*, Brescia, Tosio Martinengo Pinacoteque.

accentuate the way the protagonists loom up in the foreground and hence emphasizes their powerful presence. In this sense there are very significant comparisons that can be made with similar solutions we see in the **Women Working on Pillow Lace** (*The Sewing School*) and in **Tapping Wine** (private collection; M. Gregori, *Giacomo Ceruti,* Cinisello Balsamo 1982, pp. 433-434, nos. 55, 57), two paintings in the so-called Padernello cycle, the large series of pauperistic canvases Ceruti painted during his long stay in Brescia from 1721 to 1736.

The congruity with Ceruti's language suggested by these compositional choices is confirmed even further on the basis of the more strictly stylistic prerogatives of the canvas characterized by a diluted and essential texture, achieved with great speed and in some points limited to little more than a light glaze, completely *à plat* (see, for example, the kneeling man's blue breeches). These features are all shared by the painter's early works, from the portraits done at the beginning of the 1720s to the earlier examples of the Padernello cycle such as the **Two Old Beggars** or **The Dwarf** (private collection; Gregori,

1982, pp. 432-433, nos. 50, 53).

The most interesting fact, however, is that as in the *Beggars,* in our painting the restrained use of the medium blends not only with a surprising narrative immediacy, but also with a great ability in naturalistic study that comes across here in the rapid but extremely effective and accurate rendering of the details of the clothing such as the shoes with metal buckles, the hose cross-gartered below the knee, or the worn tailcoat made of shoddy fabric. Not to mention where the artist achieves his most remarkable results in this scene as he captures reality in rendering the dog's thick coat with magnificent effects of realism and light. Ceruti also emphasizes the definition of the rough, gnarled hands which recall those of the Cobblers in the Pinacoteca Tosio Martinengo, Brescia (Gregori, 1982, p. 435, no. 61; fig. 1). However, this harmony with the language of his early canvases is broken by the faces of the two protagonists distinguished by enraged and almost caricatural expressivity: this is quite unusual in the Lombard painter's work that is usually free of similar physiognomical exaggerations. Based on the "customs" of

earlier genre scenes and specifically the slightly stereotyped repertoire of a specialist such as Giacomo Francesco Cipper, called Todeschini (1664-1736), this more anecdotal component should actually be interpreted as a clue to a very early dating for the canvas making it reasonable to assume a date prior to even many of the earliest paintings in the Padernello cycle and therefore, not far from 1720.

Recent studies have, in fact, focused on the important role that the vast Lombard output of the prolific Todeschini played in Ceruti's development as a genre scene painter. In addition to serving as a fundamental reference in terms of subject choices, Todeschini - at least in the beginning - gave his young Milanese colleague important suggestions in the area of stylistic guidelines. A precise indication in this sense comes from a painting such as the *Card-players* formerly in the Sciltian Collection (and now at the Pinacoteca Tosio Martinengo, Brescia; Gregori, 1982, p. 431, no. 44; fig. 2). That canvas is unanimously dated nearly at the beginning of Ceruti's catalogue and it seems very important to note (especially in the face of the boy on the right) a propensity

for a highly charged and overstated rendering of the faces which in many ways is similar to what we see in *The Brawl*.

Furthermore, that the typologies of the figures in our painting are not foreign to Ceruti's language is confirmed by the comparison offered by one of the rare religious paintings from the artist's Brescia period, that is *Saint Apollonius Blessing Saints Faustinus and Jovita* in the parish church at Bione (Gregori, 1982, p. 442, no. 91), which is most likely datable around the 1720s. The gaunt profile of one of the two martyred saints is surprisingly similar to that of the standing man in *The Brawl,* almost allowing us to understand how in the earlier days, the artist had not yet entirely separated the expressive key of his genre scenes from the more flowing and more relaxed, so to speak, modus operandi of his religious scenes.

Finally, the iconographic contents of the painting deserve a word or two: they are based on a very unusual theme in the vast repertoire of genre scenes. Although it had already been dealt with by some leading genre scenes painters in the first half of the seventeenth century (for example, there is

The Musicians' Brawl by Georges de La Tour; Los Angeles, J. Paul Getty Museum, 1625-1630), the brawl as a subject did not seem to enjoy consistent success in the following decades. From our standpoint and in light of the foregoing considerations, it is worthwhile to mention that Todeschini himself dealt with the theme on several occasions, giving the finest interpretation in the big *The Card-players' Brawl* conserved in a private collection in Bergamo for which a dating has been proposed in the mature phase of his career (M.S. Proni, *Giacomo Francesco Cipper detto il "Todeschini"*, Soncino 1994, pp. 114, no. 37). However, it is entirely likely that the Austrian painter had worked on the same subject in earlier years and in this way blazed the trail for the younger Ceruti who, in turn, and certainly after the painting presented here, would return to the depiction of a fight in more subdued tones in *The Brawling Porters* painted for the Padernello cycle (Gregori, 1982, p.435, no. 62).

The presentation of the subject in this *Brawl* appears decidedly more original: what is usually portrayed as a barehanded fight is transformed into a scene of fierce violence abetted by the gun. This detail, which gives the scene a surprisingly modern accent contributes, to transforming it into a "snapshot of crime news" and which the painter magnificently succeeds in conveying its crude and almost unseemly intensity.

Francesco Frangi

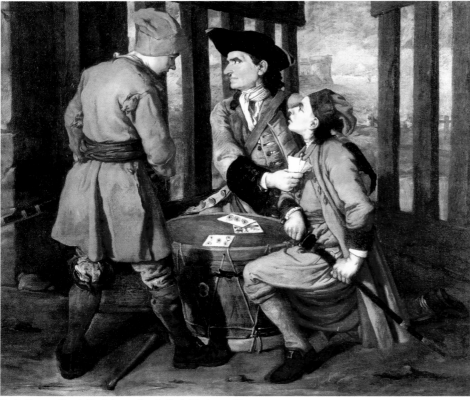

Fig 2. Giacomo Ceruti, *Card-players*, Brescia, Tosio Martinengo Pinacoteque.

MICHELE MARIESCHI
1711 - Venice - 1743

Venice, the Grand Canal with the church of San Stae, 1742 - 1743

Oil on canvas
32.7 x 44.7 in / 83.4 x 114 cm

PROVENANCE
Comtesse Benedetti, Paris;
Her sale, Paris, Hôtel Drouot, 12th-13th June
1912, lot 11 (as by Canaletto and misidentified
as *The church of the Redentore on the Giudecca);*
Bought by Madame de Saint Alary, Paris;
With Steffanoni, Bergamo;
With Pietro Accorsi, Turin;
Paris, Bruni-Tedeschi collection, after 1971;
Private Collection, Europe

LITTERATURE
R Toledano, *Michele Marieschi. L'opera
completa,* Milan 1988, p. 113, no.V.34.2
(whereabouts unknown);
R Toledano, *Michele Marieschi. Catalogo
Ragionato,* 2nd edn. revised and corrected,
Milan 1995, p. 120, no. V.42 (whereabouts
unknown);
F. Montecuccoli degli Erri-F. Pedrocco, *Michele
Marieschi. La vita, l'ambiente, l'opera,* Milan
1999, p. 240 (whereabouts unknown).

For many years this painting was known to
scholars only from a photograph in Antonio
Morassi's archive. Since its reappearance, it has
been confirmed by Professor Ralph Toledano
as one of Michele Marieschi's most outstanding
works, in exceptionally fine condition.

The scene is centred on the church of San
Stae, about two-thirds of the way up the Grand
Canal on the southern side. By choosing a
frontal view, Marieschi presents an open-ended
panorama in which the intricate buildings of
Venice shimmer between the ruffled, turquoise
water of the canal and the pale blue sky over
which light clouds drift. Gilded gondolas and
black, everyday craft dart about on the water,
animating the foreground and pushing out
beyond the boundaries of the picture. The large
size and lively handling of this painting make
it one of Marieschi's finest works, imbued with
the drama and fantasy that characterize his
vision of Venice.

Fig 1. Michele Marieschi, *View of the Grand Canal at San Stae,*
private collection.

This view was not engraved by Marieschi and
the subject is found in only one other, smaller
painting by him, *The Grand Canal with San
Stae* (22 x 33.2 in / 56 x 84.5 cm; with Richard
Green in 1985; private collection; Toledano
1995, op. cit., 1995, pp. 118-119, no. V.41;
F Montecuccoli degli Erri and F Pedrocco, op.
cit., p. 239, no. 19, illus. in colour; fig. 1). The
main subject is also the church of San Stae, but
taken from a closer viewpoint and a less broad
panorama, cutting off part of the façades of the
Palazzo Foscarini-Giovanelli to the left and the
Palazzo Contarini to the right. Less sky and
water is shown, giving this painting a much less
spacious and airy feeling than the present one.

In the present painting, from left to right,
Marieschi depicts the eighteenth century façade
of Palazzo Foscarini-Giovanelli, attributed
to the architect Giuseppe Sardi ; the Rio
della Pergola, and the pretty pink baroque
building of the Scuola dei Tiraoro e Battioro
(Goldsmiths), by Antonio Gaspari, 1711. In the
centre of the composition is the dazzling white
façade of San Stae (Sant' Eustachio in Venetian
dialect), flanked by the gothic Palazzo Priuli-
Bon which became the property of the Dandolo
family, then the imposing, classical Palazzo
Contarini. This was reduced to ashes by a fire
in the nineteenth century and in its place is a
garden. At the far right is the early fifteenth
century Palazzo Duodo. Marieschi painted this
view from the right bank of the Grand Canal,
sitting at the level of Palazzo Barbarigo.

The façade of San Stae epitomizes eighteenth
century baroque splendour. Its general
structure is conceived in a Palladian spirit, in
the way that a smaller pediment is enclosed
within a larger one (hence the confusion that
arose with Palladio's church of the Redentore
in the cataloguing of this painting in the 1912
auction). Funded by Doge Alvise Mocenigo,
whose family palazzo lies down the calle to
the right, San Stae was built by Domenico
Rossi *circa* 1709, after twelve previous projects
had been rejected. A lavish programme of
sculptures was commissioned from Tarsia,
Torretto, Baratta, Cabianca and Corradini to
decorate the church. Corradini executed the
three figures that crown the façade: Faith and
Hope to left and right, with the Redeemer at
the apex.

There are three richly carved and gilded
gondolas, of which two are decorated with
a double-headed eagle. They could as well
belong to the Giustiniani family, on whose
crest the fabled birds figure, or to the
Imperial Ambassador. Their presence made

Fig 2. Michele Marieschi, *Rialto Bridge with the Entry of the
Patriarch,* Claydon House, National Trust.

Montecuccoli and Pedrocco express the
opinion that the present painting is of the same
date as the one representing *The arrival of the
Patriarch Francesco Antonio Correr near the
Rialto Bridge,* documented in 1735 as sold to
Marshal von der Schulenburg (Claydon House,
Bucks, NT; cf. Toledano 1995, p. 75, no.
V.14; fig. 2), which shows similar gondolas.
Professor Toledano, however, considers this
insufficient evidence, which does not take into
consideration the style of the present painting.

Toledano asserts that the particularly soft
range of colours in the present painting, the
subtlety of its palette, very different from the
darker palette of the Schulenburg picture,
indicates the last phase of Marieschi's short
career. It is an attempt to emulate the more
classical spirit of Canaletto, without betraying
his own unmistakable rococo touch that
flourishes in the curlicues of the waves in
the foreground and the façades of buildings
cleverly described in rich impasto.

Indeed, never before did he translate with
brushes onto canvas the moving reflection of the
buildings in the waters of the Canal with such
delicacy. The feeling of liberty, of optimistic
light which pervades this representation of
San Stae is the sign of the ultimate maturity
expressed by the artist.

Another fact confirms Toledano's dating.
The present composition does not appear
in *Magnificentiores selectioresque urbis
Venetiarum prospectus,* the album of etchings
published by Marieschi in 1741. This records
pictures already made by the artist, as a
sentence in the complete title of the book states
('*quos olim…in plerisque tabulis depinxit*': that
before…in multiple pictures he painted). This
indicates that the present painting was
executed after the 1741 publication, in the
very short number of years before Marieschi's
untimely death in 1743.

ANTONIO JOLI
Modena 1700 - 1777 Naples

The Royal Palace of Aranjuez from the North-East, with King Ferdinand VI of Spain and Queen Mária Bárbara of Braganza on the Royal Barge, 1750 - 1755

Oil on canvas
22.3 x 38.6 in / 56.6 x 98 cm

This painting depicts the palace at Aranjuez, the favourite royal residence of King Ferdinand VI of Spain and his wife Mária Bárbara of Braganza. Lying 47 km to the south of Madrid it had been begun under Philip II in 1574 to designs by Juan de Herrera. In 1715 Philip V extended the palace but is was partly destroyed by fire soon after in 1748, allowing the new King Ferdinand to rebuild much of it, to designs by Giacomo Bonavía.

Each year Ferdinand's court spent the period between Easter and St. John's day at Aranjuez, where they were entertained by, amongst others, the great castrato Carlo Broschi (1702-1782) called Farinelli (fig. 1). The famous castrato wrote a manuscript entitled *Fiestas Reales en el Reinaldo de Fernando VI,* now in the Biblioteca del Palazzo Reale di Madrid. The manuscript, enriched by drawings of ceremonial boats, barges and costumes, lists the diverse lyrical spectacles that were produced under his direction between 1747 and 1758. Indeed it was Farinelli who on the death of the Bolognese painter Giacomo Pavia in 1749 invited Antonio Joli to the Spanish court in order to paint theatrical scenery at Aranjuez and in the Teatro del Buen Retiro in Madrid. Joli remained in Spain until 1754 but continued to work for the Spanish Crown from Italy, completing for example two large canvases depicting The Embarkation of Charles III from Naples in 1759 (See J. Urrea Fernandez, *La Pintura Italiana del Siglo XVIII en España,* 1977, p. 155, reproduced plate XXXVI). During Joli's stay in Spain there were seven such celebrations for which the artist helped design decorations. In the case of open air festivals, such as the one depicted here, the boats were usually heavily adorned.

As well as the present work, four autograph versions of this view exist: one in the Palazzo Reale, Naples (See J. Urrea Fernandez, op. cit., p. 156; fig. 2); another sold Christie's, London 7 July 1989, lot 110; another sold Sotheby's, Madrid 20 February 1992, lot 13 and, finally, one in an Irish private collection as referenced by Toledano in 2006 (Cf. R. Toledano, Antonio Joli, Milan 2006, p. 258, no. S.IX.2). With regards the work (oil on canvas, 77.5 x 125 cm) sold at Christie's, London in 1989, with a *pendant* depicting *The church and the piazza of Sant'Antonio at Aranjuez* (Cf. R. Toledano, op. cit., p. 256, S.IX.1), a comparison with the present work reveals that only a couple of the figures and the vegetation differ. The royal barge is in the centre of the painting, while Farinelli is at the stern of the boat to the left and the musicians are spread across other boats. Members of the royal court meander on the lawn in the foreground enjoying the music.

Fig 1. Bartolomoeo Nazari, *Portrait of Farinelli,* London, Royal College of Music.

Fig 2. Antonio Joli, *View of Aranjuez Palace and Gardens,* Naples, Royal Palace.

GIOVANNI PAOLO PANINI

Piacenza 1691 - 1765 Rome

Architectural Capriccio with an Apostle preaching, 1755 - 1760

Oil on canvas
20.6 x 29 in / 52.9 x 73.5 cm
Signed with initials and inscribed, lower right: I.P.P. ROMAE.

PROVENANCE
London, Christie's, 24 November 1967, lot 76.

LITERATURE
F. Arisi, *Gian Paolo Panini e i fasti della Roma del '700*, Rome 1986, p. 476, no. 497.

The painting depicts an apostle preaching amidst ancient ruins, of which we can recognize the Pyramid of Cestius and the Temple of the Sibyl at Tivoli on the right. According to Ferdinando Arisi, this painting can be dated around the final years of Panini's career when he had reached the peak of his fame and had been elected to the post of *Principe* of the Accademia di San Luca in Rome in 1754.

In the 1750s, in addition to Panini's son, Francesco, his pupils included artists of the calibre of Hubert Robert and Jean-Honoré Fragonard, who had studied perspective with Giovanni Paolo at the Accademia di Francia in Rome. With regards Robert, Professor Arisi says: "In the paintings from this period, some contribution by his favorite student is very likely, also because the master was very busy with important commissions (…) even though it is practically impossible to identify these parts" (Cf. F. Arisi, *Gian Paolo Panini e i fasti della Roma del '700*, Roma 1986, pp. 170-73). In our painting, we may be able to distinguish the hands of Panini's pupils in some of the details such as the marble relief and the statue on the right.

During this period Panini was occupied

with the "Views of Ancient and Modern Rome" - a commission for the Comte de Stainville, future Duc de Choiseul, then the French ambassador to Rome. This series was the greatest project of the artist's career, and indeed the count was one of Panini's best clients between 1754 and 1757 and in fact, the young Hubert Robert came to Rome in 1754 as part of his retinue. In addition, Panini had to satisfy the huge demand for paintings from tourists passing through the Eternal City on the Grand Tour. These souvenir hunters wanted to take home paintings in which the most famous archeological monuments were easily recognizable. Panini's imaginary landscapes with striking combinations of ancient ruins were particularly suited to their wants.

The exchange with French artists during this, the last phase of his career, gradually lightened and refined Panini's palette. According to Arisi, some of Panini's paintings from 1755-1760 "are of such typically French taste and sensitivity that they could even be attributed to Watteau" (Cf. F. Arisi, op. cit., p. 173). In his entry on the present painting, the scholar confines the dating starting from "very clear air in the composition" (Cf. F. Arisi, op. cit., p. 476), an element that is similar to the canvas in the Vitetti collection in Rome (Cf. F. Arisi, op. cit., n. 491, p. 474; fig. 1) depicting *Ruins with the Borghese Vase and Small Figures* dated 1758. From the stylistic standpoint, this picture is distinguished by the quick, wide and fluid brushstrokes that are typical of the last phase of Panini's career. The two paintings share yet another feature: the female figure in the center of the scene in a yellow dress with fullwhite sleeves is almost identical to the one on the right in the Vitetti painting.

Fig 1. Giovanni Paolo Panini, *Ruins with Borghese Vase and Characters*, Rome, private collection.

FRANCESCO GUARDI
1712 - Venice - 1793

Piazza San Marco, looking West, from the Campo di San Basso, 1757 - 1758

Oil on canvas
13.2 x 22.5 in / 33.7 x 57.2 cm

PROVENANCE
England, Private collection.

Francesco Guardi, the last real protagonist of 18th century Venetian vedutismo, spent the first thirty years of his working life as a painter of figures and copyist in his family's studio, where he distinguished himself completing the altar-pieces made by his brother Antonio (1699-1760) with landscapes, still lifes, and floral decorations. In the mid 1760s, painting vedute and *capricci* took over as his main activity, allowing him to fully express the depths of his sensitivity and the poetic aspects of his pictorial genius.

It is possible that Francesco Guardi had started making *vedute* after Canaletto (1697-1768) left for London in May 1746, but none of his known paintings can be dated with any certainty to before 1755, the year of the return in Venice of the celebrated artist (Canaletto is documented in Venice on 12 December 1755, *terminus ante quem* for his return; Montecuccoli degli Erri, *Canaletto incisore,* Venice 2002, pp. 6-7). No direct link between the two painters has been established, despite apparently being underscored by the Venetian patrician Pietro Gradenigo's note of 25th April 1764, which described Guardi as a "good scholar of the famous Canaletto" (L. Livan, *Notizie d'Arte tratte dai Notatori e dagli Annali del N.H. Pietro Gradenigo,* Venice 1942, p. 106); but the starting point for Guardi's

vedute was undoubtedly the work of the older master, etchings of views of Venice, wide-angle drawings of the Piazza San Marco end of the lagoon, such as the paintings commissioned by Consul Smith (c. 1684-1770) and works in other Venetian collections. Again, during the decades to follow, while remaining an assiduous interpreter of Canaletto and continuing to draw inspiration from the master's compositions, right from the outset Guardi played with the perspective, widened the spaces, warmed the colour tones and emphasized the variations in light. The figures in the early paintings, while clearly derivative of Canaletto, are already distinctive shapes, some rather more square, others slim, elongated and narrow, with small heads. These characteristics are all true of this beautiful painting and, as a very rare new early work by Guardi, its discovery is particularly exciting.

The painting draws on Canaletto's etching entitled *Le Procuratie Nuove e S. Ziminian* (Fig 1), from the famous *Vedute Altre prese da i Luoghi altre ideate* series, first published in Venice after Joseph Smith's appointment as British Consul, on 9 June 1744, and dedicated to him (the Canaletto etchings were executed in the early '40s but the date of the first published print is unknown; F. Montecuccoli degli Erri believes it dates to 1752. See Montecuccoli degli Erri, 2002, *Canaletto incisore,* op. cit., pp. 81-98).

The view is totally unreal, built from several

different drawings taken from life, as was the custom with the *vedutisti*. The process of building a painting from a print was already particular to Guardi. He chose a wider canvas in order to broaden Piazza San Marco, putting a greater distance between the two backdrops to the view, the north corner of the Basilica and the edge of the Bell Tower. The entire west side of the Piazza is depicted and Sansovino's façade on the ancient Church of San Geminiano, which was shut down in 1807 and later pulled down to make way for The Napoleonic Wing, is positioned more centrally. The perspective of the Basilica, with a highly-foreshortened base and the column of Sant'Alipio portal set off-axis, is rendered with a freedom unknown to Canaletto. The Procuratie Nuove, depicted with fewer arcades and windows, are taken from a smaller angle and consequently the two flag-poles have been shifted towards the middle of the Piazza and spaced out. The contours of their bronze bases, chef d'œuvres by Alessandro Leopardi (m. 1523 or 1524) and made under Doge Leonardo Loredan (1501-1521), are merely sketched in in the etching, while the painting shows the exceptionally beautiful sculptural decorations in detail, allegories of the power and sagacity of the Venetian Republic.

Various other details, left out of the print, are testament to the fact that Guardi did not think of Canaletto's works in terms of models to be copied, but as points of reference from which to start, to be transformed through his own artistic vision and completed with other drawings taken from life. The same process applies to the painting representative of Guardi's early period, based on another etching by Canaletto, *The Piazzetta, Looking toward San Giorgio Maggiore,* Museo Civico, Treviso (A. Morassi, *Guardi. L'opera completa di Antonio e Francesco Guardi,* Venice 1975, vol. l, pp. 36-369, no. 361, figs. 385, 386; fig. 1).

Antonio Morassi has catalogued three different paintings of this composition, conserved in private and public collections, regarded as "early works" and close in terms of chronology (A. Morassi, *Guardi. L'opera completa ...,* op. cit, vol. 1, p. 375, nos. 342-344; vol. 2, figs. 369-371). Like Canaletto, Guardi repeatedly depicted the same views, clearly for commercial ends, but it is the author's opinion that only one of the three versions, a painting in a Swiss private collection (before 1975. A. Morassi, *Guardi. L'opera completa ...op. cit,* vol. 1, p. 375, no. 344; vol. 2, fig. 371), is in fact in the artist's hand. It forms part of a series of

Fig 1. Canaletto, *Le Procuratie Nuove e S. Ziminian,* etching.

four views of San Marco (another in the same collection, the other two in the the Bildenden Künste Academy, Vienna. A. Morassi, *Guardi. L'opera completa* ..., *op. cit*, vol. 1, p. 388, no. 413, pp. 381-382, no. 379, pp. 382-383, no. 384; vol. 2, figs. 433, 402, 405, 406), executed after the Canaletto etchings in the early '60s, with vigorous brush-strokes, highly contrasting light and shade effects and large figures that point to the considerable influence of paintings by the young Canaletto.

There is a known preliminary drawing for this composition, formerly in the collection of Paul Wallraf (A. Morassi, *Guardi. Tutti i disegni di Antonio, Francesco e Giacomo Guardi,* Venice 1975, pp. 136-137, no. 330, fig. 326); the sheet is shaded in watercolour, the fine lines of the architecture, delicate use of watercolour and "angular", sharply sketched figures, are similar to some of the drawings based on the plein air sketches that can unquestionably be dated to 1757-1758, such as *The Lagoon from the Fondamenta Nuove* (A. Morassi, *Guardi. Tutti i disegni ...op. cit.*, p. 149, no. 399, fig. 329) and *A View of the Zattere at the Punta di Santa Marta* (A. Morassi, *Guardi. Tutti i disegni ..., op. cit,* p. 149, no. 400, fig. 404; both location unknown).

The chronology of the drawing helps to date this painting. Another known drawing of this composition, the quick sketch without figures, which shows the flag-poles in different positions, in the Kupferstichkabinett, Berlin (A. Morassi, *Guardi. Tutti i disegni ..., op. cit,* p. 136, no. 329, fig. 329), belongs to a later period; like this painting, it shows a portion of the second arch of the north side of the Basilica that is missing in the print.

The drawing previously in the Wallraf collection was clearly made for this painting, which was the only one to have been executed shortly thereafter. It belongs to Francesco Guardi's early period, when he interpreted the mature Canaletto with a more pictorial brush-stroke and a personal choice of warm brown tones, choosing a rosy grey for the illuminated parts. The figures retain the same proportions

Fig 3. Francesco Guardi, *The Lagoon and the Fort of San Nicolò di Lido,* Cambridge, Fitzwilliam Museum.

as those in Canaletto's etching, and by and large the same shapes, yet they have become different, drawn in a particular range of colours, from the browns broken up by some white and blue strokes, dotted with red, as in Canaletto, yet more intense, so as to lead the observer's eye from the foreground into the view. A clear light reaches from the shadowy foreground up to the church of San Geminiano, highlighting the colours and details. Each element of the composition has been studied to recreate the atmosphere and fascination of an everyday scene in the most beautiful place in the world, where senators and citizens, merchants and boatmen meet. As is usual in Guardi's early work, the stone pavement in Piazza San Marco bears no trace of the Istrian marble overlay with its geometrical pattern, designed by the architect Andrea Tirali and executed from February 1723. It is interesting to note that Guardi shifted the figures of the two women to the right, close to the cloth shop, so as to "exhibit" the coloured merchandise. The dog-shapes serve as a sort of signature.

This painting belongs to the period during which Francesco Guardi also worked for his first major English clients, Sir Brook Bridges who visited Padua and probably also Venice in the summer of 1757 and John Montagu, Lord Brundenell, who was in Venice from September 1758 until early 1760 (F. Russell, *Guardi and the English Tourist,* "The Burlington Magazine", CXXXVIII, 1996). A number of works inspired by Canaletto belong to this

period, among them the previously-mentioned *The Piazzetta,* Looking toward San Giorgio Maggiore, Museo Civico, Treviso (A. Morassi *Guardi. L'opera completa ..., op. cit,* vol. 1, pp. 368-369, no. 361, figs. 385, 386). Guardi was painting on canvases of standard dimensions at that time; the measurements of this painting are very similar to those of a series of views of the Lagoon, with similar elongated and narrow figures with small heads, as in the two pendants in the Fitzwilliam Museum, Cambridge, *The Lagoon and the Fort of San Nicolò di Lido* (A. Morassi *Guardi. L'opera completa ..., op. cit,* vol. 1, p. 429, no. 639; vol. 2, fig. 602; 32 x 52,8 cm; fig. 3) and *The Lagoon Looking Towards Murano from the Fondamenta Nuova* (A. Morassi, *Guardi. L'opera completa ..., op. cit,* vol. 1, p. 432, no. 658; vol. 2, fig. 613; 31,7 x 52,7 cm; fig. 3) together with another pair, now separated, in the Kunsthaus, Zurich (A. Morassi, *Guardi. L'opera completa ..., op. cit,* vol. 1, p. 429, n. 640; vol. 2, fig. 603; 31 x 52 cm) and Gallerie De Jonckheere, Paris - Brussels (A. Morassi, *Guardi. L'opera completa ..., op. cit,* vol. 1, p. 425, no. 617; vol. 2, fig. 585; 31 x 51,5 cm). As in this painting, the red colour dots stand out against the pearl-grey tones. In the 1758 painting depicting *The Feast of Giovedì Grasso in the Piazzetta,* formerly in the collection of Mario Crespi, Milan (A. Morassi *Guardi. L'opera completa ...op. cit,* vol. 1, p. 362, no. 280; vol. 2, fig. 309; 32 x 54 cm; fig. 4), smaller figures populate Piazza San Marco, but, as in this picture, the Procuratie Nuove have a smaller number of arches and windows and similar thin chimneys, and are rendered in the same way, with black brush-strokes that pick out the architectural and decorative details.

Francesco Guardi guaranteed the continuity of *vedutismo* and the collection of his work almost until the fall of the Republic. The similarity of his early works to those of Canaletto proved decisive for his success among the British Grand Tour collectors. The above-mentioned note from Pietro Gradenigo, which refers to the two *vedute* of Venice commissioned from Guardi by an "English foreigner", confirms that his later works, bearing his personal stamp, continued to attract. In the catalogue for the sale of the collection of John Strange, an English resident in Venice from 1773 to 1788, compiled in 1799, the 436 items included fifteen paintings by Guardi, including views of his villa at Paese.

Bozena Anna Kowalczyk

Fig. 2. Francesco Guardi, *The Piazzetta, Looking toward San Giorgio Maggiore,* Treviso, Museo Civico.

Fig 4. Francesco Guardi, *The Feast of Giovedì Grasso in the Piazzetta,* formerly Mario Crespi collection, Milan.

GIOVANNI ANTONIO CANAL CALLED IL CANALETTO
1697 - Venice - 1768

View of Dolo at the bank of the Brenta, also called The lock at Dolo and The Brenta-sluice between Padua and Venice, 1763

Oil on canvas
12.2 x 17.7 in / 31 x 45 cm

INSCRIPTION:
On the reverse on the wedged stretcher old stamp: 715 J; with brush: No.4; old label with handwritten marking and title: "No. 2031 / Canaletto / Vue de Dolo sur le bord de la Brenta / M. Beurdeley"; another small label with Nr. 1287.
On reverse on the canvas marked by old hand: Auguste Chatelain.

PROVENANCE
Auguste Chatelain (inscription on the relining canvas);
Alfred Beurdeley (1847-1919), Paris; his sale, Georges Petit, Paris, 7 May 1920, lot 141;
Wilhelm von Bode (1845-1929), Berlin;
His son-in-law Professor Bruns, Berlin, and by inheritance.
Private Collection, Europe.

EXHIBITIONS
Berlin, *Gemälde Alter Meister aus Berliner Besitz,* 1925, no. 13;
Turin, Palazzo Bricherasio, *Canaletto e Bellotto: l'arte della veduta,* 2008, no. 99.

LITERATURE:
H.A. Fritzsche, *Bernardo Bellotto genannt Canaletto,* Burg b. Magdeburg, 1936, p.107, under no. VG32;
W.G. Constable, *Canaletto: Giovanni Antonio Canal 1697 - 1768,* London 1962 and subsequent editions revised by J.G. Links, II, no. 373(b);
Z. Dobos, in *Treasures of Venice: Paintings from the Museum of Fine Arts, Budapest,* exhibition catalogue (Atlanta, Seattle and Minneapolis), Minneapolis 1995, p. 222, note;
B.A. Kowalczyk (ed.), *Canaletto e Bellotto: l'arte della veduta,* exhibition catalogue, Turin 2008, p. 242, no. 99 (illustrated in color p. 243).

This painting is a recent discovery and new addition to Canaletto's catalogue. As indicated on the relining canvas it comes from the Auguste Chatelain collection; a label attached to the stretcher mentions tells that it was part of A. Beurdeley's collection as a Canaletto (1847-1919) (F. Lugt, *Marques de collections,* Amsterdam 1921, no. 421, pp. 72-75), and was sold as such in 1920 at the Galerie Georges Petit, in Paris (lot 141). It was first cited by H.A. Fritzsche as an anonymous worked based on the etching *The Lock at Dolo* (R. Bromberg, *Canaletto's Etchings,* London & New York 1974, pp. 66-71, no. 6), when it was in the Berlin collection of Professor Bruns, Wilhelm von Bode's son-in-law and heir (1845-1929). W.G. Constable who wrote that he is unaware of autograph paintings of this scene, suggests that it is by an imitator of Canaletto, and Z. Dobos maintains the same opinion.

When the painting appeared on the German antique market it was considered to be by Bellotto; and, indeed in stylistic terms it is close to works in the "sometimes attributed to Bellotto" grouping because of the dark tones, the swirls and the strong *chiaroscuro* which are typical of the latter part of Canaletto's career following his return from London during the second half of 1755. Some of these pieces, such as this painting, are composed similarly to the most beautiful etchings in the series *Vedute Altre prese da i Luoghi altre ideate,* published in Venice after Joseph Smith was appointed British Consul on 16 June 1744. The version acquired by the Budapest Museum of Fine Arts in 1978 (J.G. Links, *A Supplement to W.G. Constable's Canaletto: Giovanni Antonio Canal 1697 - 1768,* London, 1998, pp. 35-36, no. 373*; fig. 1), that is very similar in terms of style and nearly identical in size, was known to S. Kozakiewicz when it was in a private Hungarian collection and is mentioned by the Polish scholar as one of the few examples of the collaboration between Canaletto and his nephew, Bellotto (S. Kozakiewicz, *Bernardo Bellotto,* London, 1972, I, p. 40, II, p. Z 294). A recent restoration has brought to light the artist's signature on the verso of the original canvas: "Io Zuea Antonio Canal deto il Canaletto, feci" - which is similar to the inscription on two other paintings - along with the date 1763. A third version that formerly belonged to the Marchesa Feltrinelli is now in a private collection in Padua (Links, 1998, *op. cit.,* p. 35, no. 371*). When each of the painted versions are compared to the etching, and they are very close to the size of the plate, we see the same composition of houses and the lock, with the *burchiello* about to depart, but the figures are different. There are no known works by Bellotto with the same composition. The only painting that speaks to the nephew's visit to the Dolo in 1742 is the *Mills at the Dolo* in a private collection (Kozakiewicz, 1972, *op. cit.,* no. 29).

Bozena Anna Kowalczyk

Fig 1. Canaletto, *The Lock at Dolo,* Budapest Museum of Fine Arts.

GIANDOMENICO TIEPOLO
1727 - Venice - 1804

The Tooth-puller, 1762 - 1770

Oil on canvas
13.2 x 22.5 in / 33.7 x 57.2 cm

PROVENANCE
Mino Forti Collection, Venice (1951);
USA, Private Collection.

EXHIBITIONS
Venice, Ca' Rezzonico, *Mostra del Tiepolo*, 3 June - 7 October 1951, no. 121 (titled *The Charlatan*);
Milan, Villa Comunale, *Mostra del Settecento veneziano*, April - May 1955, no. 71.

LITERATURE
G. Lorenzetti (ed.), *Mostra del Tiepolo,* Venice 1951, p. 170;
Mostra del Settecento veneziano, Milan 1955, p. 71;
A. Mariuz, *Giandomenico Tiepolo*, Venice 1971, pp. 126, 135, 146, n. 196;
R. Pallucchini, *La vena satirica di Giandomenico Tiepolo*, in, *La pittura nel Veneto. Il Settecento,* 2 vol., II, Milan 1996, p. 579.

The subject of the tooth-puller presents a theme popularized in the 17th century by Dutch artists such as Gerard Dou (Cf. B. Aikema, *La pittura del Settecento a Venezia,* in G. Briganti (ed.), *La pittura in Italia. Il Settecento,* Milan 1989, 2 vol., I, p. 205). Interpreted here by Giandomenico Tiepolo with quick, vibrant brushstrokes, the subject is layered with satirical undertones and pokes fun at the customs of the period. "The artist examined some of the key characters of the 18th century" portraying "a society that loves charade and trickery, to the point of taking pride in forsaking its historical identity and pleasure in "getting burned" for the ephemeral amusement of false appearances; it swapped the natural for the artificial. [...] In a similar context, notwithstanding rank or riches, success was achieved by those better at fooling others. [...] and so, we have the link between the themes of carnival and the charlatan." In this painting, the connection is made with the tooth-puller, one of the many charlatans whose role in society was that of traveling surgeon, and who performed operations that were snubbed by traditional doctors (such as removing cataracts, or gall stones and, of course, pulling teeth).

The work under analysis is closely replicated in another painting (36 x 58 cm), currently in a Roman private collection, which forms part of a series of four canvases, comprising also: *The Charlatan* (34 x 58 cm), the *Triumph of Punch* (34 x 58 cm) and *The Storyteller* (37 x 58 cm). This group of paintings was previously housed in the Barbara Hutton collection, Paris and before that was owned by the diplomat Maxwell Blake, Kansas City.

Mariuz deems the *Tooth-puller* presented here: "a graphically more descriptive, autograph replica of the painting in the Blake collection". In 1996, Pallucchini expressed the same opinion. The affinity between the two works had already been noted, in 1951, by Lorenzetti, who defined the Forti *Tooth-puller* as "tasteful in its, slightly grotesque, humanity, and in the freshness of its lively colors and the bright atmosphere".

Mariuz bases his dating of the Roman group on the date 1765 that is visible on fragments of old linings. This date seems pertinent to the present work too, which may have been executed during Giandomenico's stay in Madrid (between 1762 and 1770), with his father, decorating the ceilings of the Palacio Real.

From the mid- 1750s, Tiepolo revisited these satirical social themes a number of times, with two works in the Louvre depicting *The Tooth-puller* and *The Minuet* (circa 1754); two paintings in the Museo Nacional de Arte de Cataluña, Barcelona, depicting *The Minuet* and *The Charlatan* (dated 1756 on the standard to the left); and again in the 1757 frescoes of similar genre scenes in the guest rooms of the Villa Valmarana ai Nani, Vicenza; and finally in the frescoes of the Villa Zianigo, finished in 1797 (today at Ca' Rezzonico). Each rendering produced different stylistic results, reflecting the development of the artist's technique and style as he matured. According to Mariuz, the group of works (each 40 x 64 cm) housed in the Balboa collection, Madrid, depicting *The Charlatan*, the *New World* and the *Canine Ballerinas* are contemporary with the series of paintings in the Roman private collection.

The serial production of this small nucleus of realistic, though satirical, scenes is testimony to the large number of commissions for Giandomenico's work coming from across Europe, according to Pallucchini "paintings of this subject were directly ordered by clients from Madrid". The widespread success of these works, caused Mariuz to hypothesize about another grouping, today dismembered, that also comprised this *Tooth-puller*. The scholar conjectures to the existence of a series, analogous to the Roman collection, composed of: the *Triumph of Punch* in the Statens Museum for Kunst, Copenhagen (35 x 57.5 cm; fig. 1), the *New World* in the Musée des Arts Décoratifs, Paris (36 x 62 cm; fig. 2), *The Storyteller* in the Suida Manning collection, New York (34 x 57.5 cm) and finally this *Tooth-puller*.

A subtle melancholic veil permeates the two most similar versions of *The Tooth-puller* (the present work and that in the Roman private collection) with respect to their predecessors. The ironic undertone that lies within the artist's depictions of everyday life seems to suggest a detached narrative, emphasized by the multitude of figures lined up next to each other with their backs to the observer, in a "series of anti-portraits" as Mariuz describes

Fig 1. Giandomenico Tiepolo, *Triumph of Pulcinella*, Copenaghen, Staten Museum for Kunst.

it. Giandomenico had already used this device - in the various versions of the *New World* - confirming: "Domenico's tendency to cite himself (Mariuz 1971). Amongst the onlookers Tiepolo depicts a varied representation of society: some noblemen wearing *bauta*, a number of figures in carnival masks, and women and children in costumes.

As Pallucchini notes, Goya was heavily influenced by this new artistic genre that depicted social customs in a clear and rudimentary satire, that verged on the grotesque in Tiepolo's works. According to Pallucchini, "Domenico sensed the downfall of a society in complete crisis and hinted at it through [depictions of] hilarious and bitter buffoonery".

In the easel works of the 1760s, Giandomenico's technique can be seen to have completely moved away from the stylistic lessons taught by his father which, in fact, permeate the Louvre and Barcelona paintings. There is a 1779 engraving of the Tooth-puller by Berardi, with a caption in rhyme: *"Degli error popolar schiava si rese / La plebe sempre alla ragion infesta: / Quindi de' Ciurmator la turba apprese / Con suo profitto a divenir molesta"*.

Fig 2. Giandomenico Tiepolo, *The New World*, Paris, Musée des Arts Décoratifs.

FRANCESCO GUARDI
1712 - Venice - 1793

Venice. The Lagoon and the Fort of San Niccolò at Lido, 1775 - 1785

Oil on canvas
16.5 x 26.8 in / 42 x 68 cm

PROVENANCE
Paris, Probably private collection; ('Madame de X'); by whom sold Modave Sale, Paris, Galerie Charpentier, 12 June 1936, lot 8;
M. James Adolphe Yuan Amez-Droz (d. 1976) and by descent;
USA, Private Collection.

LITERATURE
Probably J. W. Goodison and G.H. Robertson, *Fitzwilliam Museum Cambridge. Catalogue of Paintings,* vol. II, *Italian Schools*, Cambridge 1967, p. 73, no. 9.

The Forte di San Niccolò was situated at the northern end of the Venetian Lido, near the entrance of the Porto di Lido, where the Adriatic sea enters the Venetian Lagoon. During the heyday of the Venetian Republic or *Serenissima* this represented the principal access to the Venetian sea and was therefore guarded accordingly. Built in the mid-fifteenth century, the Forte di San Niccolo was called the Castelvecchio to distinguish it from the nearby fort of Sant'Andrea, the Castelnuovo, which faced it across the waters of entrance to the Lagoon, and with which it formed the front line of the Venetian sea defences. Both received their sternest test during the Turkish advances of the late 1560s prior to the great sea battle of Lepanto in 1571, and a third tower, the Torre Massimiliana was added the following century. The Forte di San Niccolò no longer stands, and the area around it is today a military zone.

Hitherto unpublished, this fine and atmospheric work is one of only a small number of views of this small fort on the northern edge of the Venetian lagoon. On a hot and calm summer's afternoon, the flags of the coastal vessels as well as that of the fort hang limply in the air, and the activities and colours of the gondolas plying their trade are mirrored in the calm water. A smaller but closely related painting on panel was formerly in the collection of Sir Bernard Eckstein and was sold at Sotheby's on 8 December 1948, lot 13 (oil on panel, 7 x 9.5 in). Two views seen from a more distant viewpoint are recorded by Morassi in the Fitzwilliam Museum, Cambridge, and a signed canvas formerly with the Koetser Gallery in Zurich (A. Morassi, *Guardi. I Dipinti,* Venice 1993, vol. I, p. 429, cat. nos. 639 and 640, reproduced vol. II, figs. 602 and 603). Both of these are relatively youthful works, and both form part of Guardi's celebrated series of *vedute lagunari* painted in the 1760s.

The present canvas is more likely of later date. Among those views taken from a closer stand-point, Goodison lists examples in the Pasquinelli collection in Milan; with Messrs. Vickers, London; with Galerie Trotti, Paris; and that in the Modave sale, sold Paris, Galerie Charpentier, 12 June 1936, lot 8. The latter of these last two was also on a canvas of very similar dimensions (41 x 67 cm) and may well be identifiable with the present lot. A related drawing in pen and brown ink and brown wash over black chalk is today in Washington,

National Gallery of Art, Samuel H. Kress Collection (Inv. no. 1963.15.13, 30 x 45.9 cm. Exhibited London, Royal Academy of Arts and Washington, National Gallery of Art, *The Glory of Venice: Art in the Eighteenth Century,* 1994-1995, no. 214, as the Forte di San Andrea; fig. 1). This is generally considered a late drawing by Guardi, dating from around 1775-1785, and a similar date of execution could therefore be proposed for the present painting.

Fig 1. Francesco Guardi, *The Fortress of San Niccolo*, Washington, National Gallery of Art.

Catalogue produced on occasion of the exhibition:
'ITALIAN PAINTINGS FROM THE 17TH TO THE 18TH CENTURIES'

7 January – 19 February 2011
At SPERONE WESTWATER
257 Bowery, New York 10002

Edited and co-ordinated by: Mira Dimitrova, Angelica Poggi and Marco Voena
Exhibition curated by: Gian Enzo Sperone and Marco Voena

Published by ROBILANT + VOENA, 2010
Copyright © 2010 ROBILANT + VOENA

ISBN: 978-0-9563650-2-6

Printed in England by Beacon Press